GROUND TRAINING FOR THE PRIVATE PILOT LICENCE

MANUAL ONE

AIR LEGISLATION, AVIATION LAW, FLIGHT RULES AND PROCEDURE

R. D. CAMPBELL

Aviation Training Publications

GRANADA

London Toronto Sydney New York

Granada Technical Books
Granada Publishing Limited
8 Grafton Street, London W1X 3LA

First published in Great Britain by Aviation Training Publications Ltd 1977
Reprinted 1979
Revised 1980
Reprinted 1982 by Granada Publishing
Reprinted 1983 and updated to meet new syllabus requirements which
  are in effect from 1983
Reprinted 1984

Copyright © 1977, 1983 R. D. Campbell

ISBN 0-246-11698-6

Printed and bound in Great Britain by
Stanley L Hunt (Printers) Ltd, Midland Road, Rushden, Northamptonshire

Nothing in this Manual must be taken as superseding the Legislation,
Rules, Regulations, Procedures and Information contained in the Air
Navigation Order, the Air Navigation (General) Regulations, Rules of the Air
and Air Traffic Control Regulations, the UK Air Pilot, NOTAMS, Aeronautical
Information Circulars, or the Recommendations, Restrictions, Limitations
and Operating Procedures published in Aircraft, Engines or Systems
Manuals and Certificates of Airworthiness, or any Civil Air Publication or
similar document published by the Civil Aviation Authority.

AOPA PRIVATE PILOT SYLLABUS
(*Aeroplanes*)
Technical Subjects

This Training Manual is one of a set of 4 specifically written to cover the Technical Subjects section of the AOPA Private Pilot Syllabus as approved by the United Kingdom Civil Aviation Authority.

In this series of Manuals, the reference information as listed in the AOPA Private Pilot Syllabus is divided into the Sections shown below.

MANUAL 1	SECTION 1	AIR LEGISLATION
	SECTION 2	AVIATION LAW, FLIGHT RULES & PROCEDURES
		AIR TRAFFIC RULES & SERVICES
MANUAL 2	SECTION 3	AIR NAVIGATION
	SECTION 4	AVIATION METEOROLOGY
MANUAL 3	SECTION 5	PRINCIPLES OF FLIGHT
	SECTION 6	AIRFRAMES & AERO ENGINES
	SECTION 7	AIRCRAFT AIRWORTHINESS
	SECTION 8	AIRCRAFT INSTRUMENTS
MANUAL 4	SECTION 9	SPECIFIC AIRCRAFT TYPE
	SECTION 10	FIRE, FIRST AID & SAFETY EQUIPMENT
	SECTION 11	AEROMEDICAL FACTS

Other Manuals in this Training Series for Instructors and Students comprise:

Flying Training for the Private Pilot Licence – Instructor Manual

Flying Training for the Private Pilot Licence – Student Manual

Supplements to both of these Manuals are currently available to cover the:–

Night Rating

Multi Engine Rating

☆　☆　☆　☆　☆　☆　☆　☆

When the revised IMC Rating Syllabus has been approved by the CAA a Training Manual will be published to cover the training requirements of this Rating.

Training Manuals for the:–

AOPA Aerobatic Certificate

AOPA Radio Navigation Certificate

will be published when the appropriate syllibi has been approved by the AOPA Instructor Committee.

Additional Manuals in this series will be published to cater for:–

Conversion onto Different Types of Aircraft
(*including Complex Types*)

Ditching and Survival Procedures.

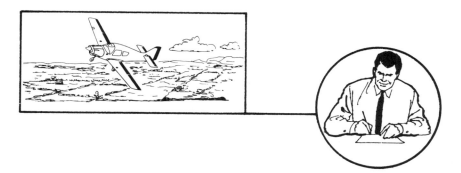

Introduction

When a person first learns to fly his immediate concentration is on learning how to control the aircraft and develop his physical reflexes to achieve judgement in handling the controls so that the aircraft does what he wants it to do.

However in flying, judgement involves two specific areas, one which relates to the development of physical skills and the other which relates to the making of correct decisions. Lack of judgement in making decisions usually stems from a lack of appreciation or failure to properly comprehend the many items of knowledge which in themselves form the basis of understanding and without which the correct decision in handling a particular situation cannot be made without a large element of luck.

In order to operate an aircraft in safety a pilot will need to develop the elements of skill and good judgement, the quality of these requirements will largely be based upon the acquisition and correct application of knowledge.

From this statement the importance of knowledge, when flying, can be appreciated. Once knowledge is gained, the appropriate skills can be developed and the basis of sound captaincy laid.

Probably the greatest difficulty in gaining the necessary knowledge relating to aircraft operation is the number of technical subjects which need to be covered. The pilot must have a sound understanding of all aspects of operating his aircraft and of the environment in which he operates. This means he will need to study and receive instruction in a wide curriculum.

The Civil Aviation Authority is responsible for laying down the privileges of a Private Pilot's Licence, and the number of flying training hours which they consider to be the minimum required for the grant of a licence. In order to ensure that the training you receive embraces all the items considered necessary to qualify you to exercise these privileges, the Civil Aviation Authority also issues a broad but specific training syllabus to cover the requirements of . . . Flight Safety.

The detailed interpretation of this syllabus, however is normally undertaken by the various individual Training Organisations, Schools, and Clubs, and by the Aircraft Owners and Pilots Association of the United Kingdom (AOPA). The training syllabus is therefore very much the responsibility of those individuals with particular knowledge and experience in the training of pilots.

It will nevertheless be the responsibility of your instructor to ensure that you have reached the necessary standard of competence in relation to aviation knowledge, skill and judgement before you apply for your written and flight tests to gain your Private Pilot Licence.

However, although it is the combined responsibility of the Civil Aviation Authority, your training organisation and your instructor to ensure you have reached the requisite standard before receiving a Private Pilot's Licence or any of its associated Ratings, the ultimate responsibilty for Flight Safety is yours and yours alone.

Remember, in the final analysis it is your knowledge, your skills and your judgement which will either result in a safe enjoyable flight, one made within your limitations and experience, or an unpleasant or hazardous event or worse . . . one suffered by you and your passengers alike, because these essential qualities were lacking.

The knowledge required by a private pilot concerns many areas and those laid down in the AOPA Private Pilot Licence Syllabus conform to the requirements of the United Kingdom Civil Aviation Authority, which are as follows:—

AIR LEGISLATION

AVIATION LAW, FLIGHT RULES & PROCEDURES
(Air Traffic Rules & Services)

AIR NAVIGATION

AVIATION METEOROLOGY

PRINCIPLES OF FLIGHT

AIRFRAMES & AERO ENGINES

AIRCRAFT AIRWORTHINESS

AIRCRAFT INSTRUMENTS

SPECIFIC AIRCRAFT TYPE

FIRE, FIRST AID & SAFETY EQUIPMENT

AEROMEDICAL FACTS

These subjects clearly cover a wide area and therefore to simplify and direct a student's task the necessary items of knowledge have been placed in 4 small manuals in a manner which directly follows the layout of the syllabus produced by the Aircraft Owners and Pilots Association, one which has been approved by the United Kingdom Civil Aviation Authority.

The subject presentation follows the sequence of the AOPA Syllabus both in the order in which the subjects are listed and in the order in which the items of any one subject appear. A series of progress tests is included at the rear of this Manual and this section contains a number of multiple choice type questions which will allow a student to monitor and self examine his learning coverage simply and efficiently.

Learning is achieved in various ways but generally two methods are paramount. One, in which reading, thinking and resolving problems plays the primary part, and the other where the person practices and develops physical skills. In flying training a student will find that both these methods of learning are employed, however, whereas learning is the act of acquiring knowledge, the purpose of it is to obtain a skill or acquire experience.

Therefore the knowledge gained through reading this Manual must be related to the understanding of those factors which concern the operation of an aircraft. If this fact is borne in mind throughout the reading of this book an important and necessary step towards pilot competence will result.

In order to organise training time efficiently it will be necessary for a student to know the depth of knowledge expected from him in each of the subject areas, and therefore in the following pages an attempt has been made to embrace both the coverage and depth of the information which is considered essential for the private pilot to understand, in order to develop the necessary skills and judgement required of a safe competent pilot. However in a Manual of this nature it would not be amiss to cover briefly the best way of tackling the methods the student should use in his learrning programme and a structured guide which outlines a recommended sequence of learning is shown on page 7.

The reason for including this guide is that, although the subject areas are contained in their individual sections throughout this Manual it would be inadvisable to read and study each page in numerical sequence until the end is reached.

For example, from the early stages of his training a pilot will, during any one flight, use items of knowledge drawn from many technical subjects. With this in mind it will be sensible to learn small portions of the various subject areas during any one learning period, e.g. your first learning period should cover the initial information given under several subject headings. Reading across from one subject to another will be in keeping with the way such knowledge is used in the cockpit and helps towards a quicker understanding of what is involved in any one of your training flights.

The guide is only a suggested one and you are free to develop your own sequence and content depending upon your own capabilities, the time you have available and your own instructor's advice and recommendations.

A further and important point when reading the subject matter is that your memory retention will be significantly improved by using an organised 'review technique'. This statement is based upon the fact that most people forget some 80% of the information they have received within 24 hours of a learning session.

Correct review technique can result in an enormous reduction in the amount which is normally forgotten. For example, a first review of the subject matter learned should take place about 10 minutes after a learning session and this review should be some 10 minutes in length. The following day a second review of the subject matter learned should be completed and this should last about 5 minutes.

A third and fourth review of 5 minutes at a time should be carried out within one week and this should be followed by a final 5 minute period one month later. After these reviews most of the knowledge gained will be implanted into your 'long term memory' and can then be recalled in the same manner as a person can recall the adress of his previous home although several years may have elapsed since he lived there.

Finally it must be realised that although this type of review sequence may seem an unnecessary chore its most significant benefit lies in its accumulative effect upon the activity of learning, thinking and recall. A person who does not find time to correctly review what he has learned will continually waste most of the effort he has put into the learning task. On the other hand a person who has developed good memory recall will be far more likely to arrive at the correct decision at the correct time when the circumstances require it, and as such he will be able to demonstrate the essential qualities of a good aircraft captain.

Acknowledgements

Acknowledgements are gratefully made to the Civil Aviation Authority and Airtour International Ltd. for their co-operation in permitting reproduction of extracts from their publications.

Acknowledgements are also made to those members of the Civil Aviation Authority, Flight Crew Licensing, Airworthiness Division, to the National Air Traffic Services, the AOPA Instructor Committee, The Panel of Examiners and to Mr. J. Jones MA Cantab for their advice and helpful suggestions which formed an important contribution to this Manual.

Study Guide

Stage 1.

Start by studying from page 1-1, **Introduction** through to page 1-11, **Issue and Renewal of Certificates of Airworthiness.**

Complete Quiz No. 1. . . .   Page Q1.

★   ★   ★   ★

Stage 2.

Continue by studying from page 2-1, **Introduction** through to page 2-22, **Altimeter Setting Procedures.**

Complete Quiz No. 3 . . .   page Q11.

★   ★   ★   ★

Stage 3.

Continue by studying from page 1-12, **Equipment of Aircraft** through to page 1-32, **Power to Prevent Aircraft Flying.**

Complete Quiz No. 2 . . .   page Q5.

★   ★   ★   ★

Stage 4.

Continue by studying from page 2-23, **Flight at Aerodromes** through to page 2-30, **Marshalling Signals.**

Complete Quiz No. 4 . . .   page Q15.

★   ★   ★   ★

Stage 5.

Continue by studying from page 2-31, **Flight Plans** through to page 2-79, **Flight Safety.**

Complete Quiz No. 5 . . .   page Q21.

★   ★   ★   ★

Quiz answers are on page Q27.

'This page intentionally left blank'

GROUND INSTRUCTION

AMENDMENT LIST No.	DATE INCORPORATED	SIGNATURE
Amendment List No 1 Incorporated		

CONTENTS

SECTION 1

CONTENTS

SECTION 2

Section   1

AIR   LEGISLATION

GROUND INSTRUCTION

AIR
LEGISLATION

Introduction

As individuals, we are required to live in an organised society and although we may dislike many of the regulations which govern us, it is clear that without some form of legislation considerable chaos would occur. This is particularly true of aviation where humans and complex products of technological engineering come together and operate as one unit in a unique and unfamiliar environment.

In an environment of this nature some form of legislation is a must and through it stem the many regulations that a pilot has to learn in order to safely control his aircraft and prevent hazard to his passengers or others.

The Governments of most countries have organisations to implement and regulate for Aviation Safety and in the United Kingdom it is the task of the Civil Aviation Authority to protect the safety and the intersts of those who fly as passengers in aircraft and the general public at large.

A simplified outline of those sections of the CAA which control the standards and safety of private pilots, aircraft and the operations of General Aviation is shown below in Fig. 1-1.

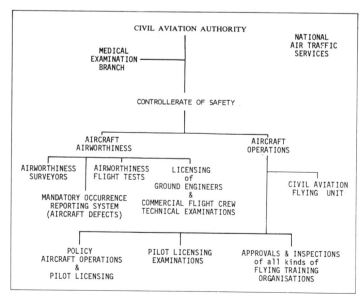

Fig. 1-1

The Legislative Documents

The main statutory documents which cover the privileges of private pilots, and the regulations concerning the operation of aircraft and the safety of passengers are the:—

    Air Navigation Order

    Air Navigation (General) Regulations

    Rules of the Air and Air Traffic Control Regulations.

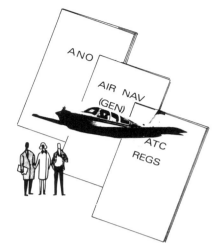

The Air Navigation Order (ANO) is the legal document which contains the written law enacted by Parliament. It contains a large number of orders known as *'Articles'* which relate to flight crew licensing and the operation of aircraft registered in, or operated within, the United Kingdom.

The ANO also contains a section of Schedules which amplify where necessary (usually in tabular form) deatils relating to the respective Articles.

The Air Navigation (General) Regulations is another legal document enacted by Parliament and it contains regulations of a general nature which in the main relate to Public Transport operations, e.g. carriage of fare paying passengers. Nevertheless some of the regulations contained in this document are applicable to the private pilot.

The Rules of the Air and Air Traffic Control Regulations is a document which has the same status as the aforementioned Orders and contains the detailed information indicated by its title.

Other publications which to a large extent precis the regulations contained in the above three documents are issued by the Civil Aviation Authority and these are listed below:—

Civil Air Publications:

    CAP53   This contains information relating to licensing and Student and Student and Private Pilot privileges.

    CAP85   This booklet contains information on Aviation Law, e.g. Rules of the Air and Air Traffic Control Regulations.

    CAP413   This booklet outlines in detail the procedures used in Radio-telephony (RTF).

All student pilots and private pilots should have a current copy of these last three publications. However the main statutory publications contain more information than private pilots need to know, and therefore to simplify your learning task the areas important to you are extracted and outlined in the following text.

Note: In relation to legislation it must be appreciated that 'only a Court of Law can interpret the law'. Therefore the reader is cautioned to the effect that the following information regarding Aviation Legislation (including the regulations concerning Licensing, Rules of the Air and Air Traffic Control) can only be covered in this manual in a manner which will enable the student pilot to obtain a broad appreciation of the subject. On those occasions when it is necessary to obtain a more detailed understanding of the finer points, reference will have to be made to the applicable sections of the relevant statutory documents.

The Air Navigation Order

To understand how this legislation applies it is first necessary to understand that aircraft are divided into different classes as shown below:

Classification of Aircraft

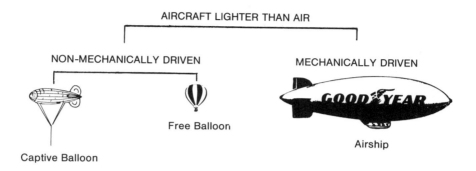

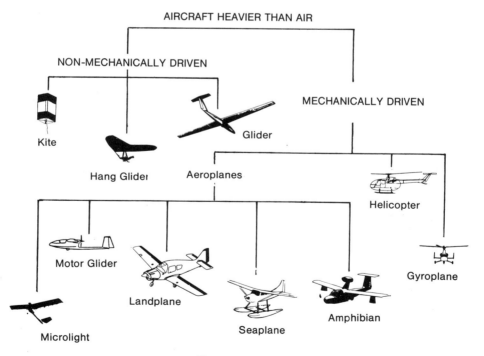

Fig. 1-2

The contents of this manual relate in the main to the operation of those aircraft which are heavier than air and which fall into the classification of *'Aeroplanes'*.

Certificate of Airworthiness to be in force

With the exception of certain special conditions, e.g. initial test flights or similar operations, an aeroplane is not permitted to be flown unless there is a valid Certificate of Airworthiness (C of A) in force at the time of the flight.

Before issuing a certificate of airworthiness the CAA must be satisfied that the individual aeroplane is fit to fly in the particular role, having regard to the design, construction, workmanship and materials used including the engine and any equipment which is necessary for the airworthiness of the aircraft. The results of flight or any other tests will also have to be assessed and found satisfactory.

A Certificate of Airworthiness is issued for all aeroplanes engaged in normal flying operations such as private and training flights, public transport (fare paying passengers) etc. or aerial work, e.g. aerial photography, survey and similar operations.

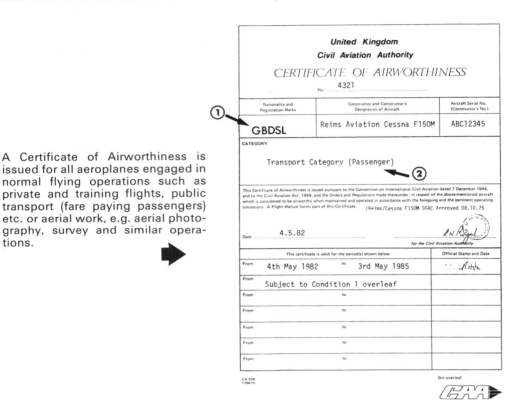

Fig. 1-3

All aircraft operating within the United Kingdom must be registered and issued with standard identification markings. However certain exceptions are made in the case of prototype aeroplanes or those engaged on specific experimental flights.

When an aeroplane is registered in the United Kingdom the registration must be made in the owners name and a '*Certificate of Registration*' will be issued which will contain the following information:−

> The Certificate number.
>
> The nationality mark of the country followed by its registration marks. The nationality mark allocated to the UK is 'G' and this is followed by four additional registration marks, e.g. **G-BDSL**. See item 1 in Fig. 1-3.

The name of the aircraft manufacturer.

The specific type of aircraft.

The aircraft serial number.

The name and address of every person who is entitled as owner to a legal interest or share of the aircraft.

The date of issue or re-issue when the ownership changes.

Note: The certificate of registration is not proof of legal ownership.

```
┌─────────────────────────────────────────────────────────────┐
│                                                             │
│                    United  Kingdom                          │
│                                                             │
│                 Civil Aviation Authority                    │
│                                                             │
│                                                             │
│          CERTIFICATE  OF  REGISTRATION  OF  AIRCRAFT        │
│                                                             │
│  1. NATIONALITY OR COMMON │ 2. MANUFACTURER    AND │ 3. AIRCRAFT SERIAL │
│     MARK AND REGISTRATION │    MANUFACTURER'S      │       NUMBER       │
│     MARK                  │    DESIGNATION OF AIRCRAFT │                │
│                           │  Piper Aircraft Corp.  │                    │
│        G-BXXX             │  Lock Haven. PA. USA.  │     654321         │
│                           │  PA 24-250             │                    │
│                                                             │
│  4. NAME OF OWNER                                           │
│                                                             │
│  5. ADDRESS OF OWNER                                        │
│                                                             │
│  6. It is hereby certified that the above described aircraft has been │
│     duly entered on the United Kingdom Register in accordance with the │
│     Convention on International Civil Aviation dated 7 December 1944, │
│     and with the Air Navigation Order 1974.                 │
│                            .............................    │
│                                                             │
│  Date of Issue.................   For the Civil Aviation    │
│                                   Authority.                │
│                                                             │
│                                   CAA ▶                     │
│                                                             │
└─────────────────────────────────────────────────────────────┘
```

Fig. 1-4

Categories — ANO Schedule 3.

An aeroplane can operate for different purposes, e.g. private flying, public transport of passengers or cargo, aerial work, etc. and the C of A will show the particular category in which the aircraft has been placed for the purpose of flight operations. See item 2, Fig. 1-3.

It is important to understand the differences between these categories otherwise a pilot may find that he is operating an aircraft in a role for which it has not been cleared, and this would be illegal. A brief explanation of the different categories applicable to aircraft (not exceeding 2730 kg) and the purposes for which an aircraft can be used is as follows:

Transport Category (Passenger) — Any purpose.

Transport Category (Cargo) — Any purpose, other than the public transport of passengers.

Aerial Work Category — Any purpose other than public transport.
Private Category   — Any purpose, other than public transport or aerial work.
Special Category   — Any purpose, other than public transport, specified in the certificate of airworthiness but not including the carriage of passengers unless expressly permitted.

Certain aircraft which do not meet the conditions for the issue of a Certificate of Airworthiness may be issued with an authorisation known as a 'Permit To Fly'.

During training, a student or private pilot will normally fly aircraft which are in the public transport (passenger) category. When flying for pleasure or recreational purposes, a pilot may be concerned with aircraft issued with a public transport (passenger), private or special category certificate of airworthiness or a permit to fly.

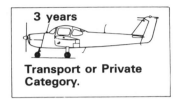

3 years

Transport or Private Category.

Transport and Private Category aircraft will normally be issued with Certificates of Airworthiness which remain valid for a period of three years.

The Special Category C of A will be valid for one year, but certain aircraft if maintained to a Maintenance Schedule approved by the CAA Airworthiness Division, may have a certificate issued valid for up to three years.

Limitations of ' Special Category'

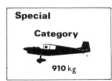

Special

Category

910 kg

Any limitation upon the use of the aircraft will be specified in the certificate. Such certification will not, in any case, permit the aircraft to be used for the purpose of public transport of flying training for reward, but may permit aerial work where appropriate.

It may also permit private use, and the hire from one person to another, of single seater aircraft of which the maximum authorised weight does not exceed 910 kg.

Aircraft may be placed in the Special Category for a variety of reasons, these are:

Private aircraft not required by the owner to be used for other than private flying.

Aircraft of which there is insufficient performance data available.

Aircraft equipped for agricultural or aerial work purposes and therefore unable to meet the requirements for Transport Category certification.

Aircraft that have been modified in such a way as to preclude their use for public transport.

Prototype aircraft that have been designed to an acceptable national airworthiness level or standard, but which are not yet eligible for the Private Category.

Amateur built aircraft, before evidence of safety has been provided.
Experimental aircraft of all kinds.

Ex-military aircraft of types closely similar to a civil counterpart.

Note: Overseas flight may require permission from the appropriate authorities but flight within the UK may be unrestricted.

 Further restrictions may also be imposed in certain conditions, and the operation of certain aircraft certificated in the Special Category may be restricted to named pilots.

Permit to Fly

In certain cases the aircraft may be eligible to be issued with a 'Permit to Fly' instead of a category of Certificate of Airworthiness and full details of this method can be obtained from the Popular Flying Association (PFA), Terminal Building, Shoreham Airport, Shoreham by Sea, Sussex BN4 5FF. The main benefits obtained by operating on a Permit to Fly lies in a more simplified maintenance procedure and lesser operating costs.

Note: The nations of the world have established an organisation (ICAO) to serve as a medium through which international planning and agreement can be reached in the areas of aircraft operation, air safety and legislation. Its headquarters are in Montreal and they act as a collating source in the implementation of standardisation on all aspects of practices and procedures used in civil aviation. In 1977 some 115 countries were member states of the International Civil Aviation Organisation.

Application of the Flight/Owner's Manual/Pilot's Operating Handbook to the Certificate of Airworthiness.

 In order to ensure that the pilot does not operate his aircraft contrary to the specific advice and instructions of the manufacturer and to relate such items as aircraft performance, limitations, weight and balance, etc. to the operation of a particular aircraft the use of the Flight Manual is integrated in the C of A by the words 'A Flight Manual Forms Part Of This Certificate'.

This is printed on the facing page of the Certificate of Airworthiness and the particular Flight Manual will be coded with the same number that appears on the top of the associated C of A. See figs 1-5 and 1-7.

When foreign manufactured aircraft are accepted and certificated on the UK aircraft register, the UK Airworthiness Authorities will normally raise a Supplement to be inserted into the Aircraft Manual. It is important for a pilot to read through this supplement very carefully as its contents may change some of the manufacturers recommended procedures contained in the main body of the manual.

United Kingdom
Civil Aviation Authority

CERTIFICATE OF AIRWORTHINESS

No. 4321

Nationality and Registration Marks	Constructor and Constructor's Designation of Aircraft	Aircraft Serial No. (Constructor's No.)
GBDSL	REIMS AVIATION Cessna F150M	ABC 12345

CATEGORY

TRANSPORT CATEGORY

This Certificate of Airworthiness is issued pursuant to the Convention on International Civil Aviation dated 7 December 1944, and to the Civil Aviation Act, 1949, and the Orders and Regulations made thereunder, in respect of the above-mentioned aircraft which is considered to be airworthy when maintained and operated in accordance with the foregoing and the pertinent operating limitations. A Flight Manual forms part of this Certificate. (Reims/Cessna F150M SGAC Approved 08.10.76

Date 2:7:82

for the Civil Aviation Authority

This certificate is valid for the period(s) shown below		Official Stamp and Date
From 2nd July 1983	to 1st July 1986	
From Subject to Condition 1 overleaf.	to	
From	to	
From	to	
From	to	
From	to	
From	to	

CA 958
170675

See overleaf

Fig. 1-5

This certificate is valid for the period(s) shown below		Official Stamp and Date
From	to	
From	to	
From	to	
From	to	
From	to	
From	to	
From	to	

Condition 1. The aircraft must be maintained in accordance with the Approved Maintenance Scedule No ARB/GPMS/FW/1972 as amended.

Condition 2.

The aircraft must be operated in accordance with the manufacturers operating instructions and limitations.

No entries or endorsements may be made on this Certificate except by an authorised person. If this Certificate is lost, the Civil Aviation Authority should be informed at once. Any person finding this Certificate should forward it immediately to the Civil Aviation Authority, Airworthiness Division, Brabazon House, Redhill, Surrey RH1 1SQ.

CAA

Fig. 1-6

However when the aircraft manual has not been specifically approved by the CAA, the following words will usually appear on the rear page of the C of A:

> *'This aircraft must be operated in accordance with the manufacturers operating instructions and limitations'*. (See Fig. 1-6).

AIRCRAFT

FLIGHT MANUAL

REIMS/CESSNA F150M

Manufacturer : REIMS AVIATION
Aérodrome de REIMS PRUNAY
51100 REIMS Marne FRANCE

CIVIL AVIATION AUTHORITY 30.8.76

French Type Certificate No. 38

Serial Number : ABC 12345 Registration Number : GBDSL

Sections : 2 - 3 - 5

"This is the flight manual which forms part of Certificate of Airworthiness Number 4321

Pages : 2-1 thru 2-6
3-1 thru 3-7
5-6, 5-7 and 5-11

This is the exact translation of the F150M French Flight Manual approved by SGAC

This aircraft should be operated in accordance with the limits specified in this Flight Manual.

THIS DOCUMENT SHOULD BE CARRIED IN THE AIRCRAFT AT ALL TIMES.

Edition 1 - August 1974
Revision 2 - August 1975

Aircraft Serial No. F15001144 on

D1055 - 13GB - Letters - 100 - 12/75

0-1

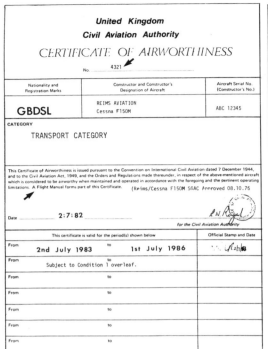

Fig. 1-7

Good operating practice dictates that the operation of any particular aircraft should be based upon that aircraft's capabilities and in the interest of safety the pilot will need to observe and use the information contained in the relevant aircraft manual or handbook.

This information will cover such various aspects as whether or not the aircraft is permitted to be operated in VFR/IFR,* by day or by night, in icing conditions, and above a certain altitude.

It will also be necessary to establish the various airframe, engine and system limitations, performance figures, stalling and (where permitted) spinning characteristics, emergency and normal procedures and any supplementary information which the CAA Airworthiness Division may require to bring to the attention of the pilot operating the aircraft.

Manuals will not usually contain information which should be common knowledge to a qualified pilot and which it is reasonably assumed the pilot will already know.

Note — The terms VFR and IFR relate to specific weather conditions and are covered later in the section dealing with *'**Air Traffic Services**'*.

Conditions for Maintaining the Validity of the C of A

The CAA may issue a C of A subject to such other conditions concerning the airworthiness of the aircraft as it thinks fit.

Operation of Aircraft Subject to Conditions Stated in the C of A

An example of this has already been covered in that when Owner's Manuals/Pilot's Operating Handbooks are used, a condition will be that the pilot operates the aircraft in accordance with the information contained in them.

Any other condition which is applicable to the operation of the particular aircraft will be typed on the rear page of the C of A. Typical examples of such other conditions are as follows:

> Condition 2. The total number of occupants (excluding children under three years old carried in the arms of passengers) may not exceed .... persons.
>
> Condition 3. Aerobatic manoeuvres are prohibited.
>
> Condition 4. The aircraft must be maintained in accordance with the Approved Maintenance Schedule No ....

Any operation of the aircraft outside these conditions will automatically render the C of A invalid. Therefore the first time you fly a particular aircraft you should read the Certificate of Airworthiness and carefully note any conditions which appear on it. Unless this check is made you may subject the aircraft to a category of operation or flight manoeuvre which is not permitted.

Requirements for Maintenance Inspections

All aircraft in the Transport or Private Category will have to be maintained and serviced in accordance with an approved maintenance schedule. Certain aircraft in the Special Category will be exempt this requirement but the C of A will then only last for one year.

However the owner of an aircraft in the Special Category may elect to maintain his aircraft in accordance with an approved maintenance schedule and in this case will usually be issued with a C of A which lasts for three years in the same way as a Transport or Private Category aircraft.

The basic maintenance schedule which is approved for fixed wing aircraft which have a maximum authorised all-up weight not exceeding 2730 kg and which operate in the Transport or Private Category is entitled LAMS/FW, and this is updated at intervals by an amendment service from the CAA Airworthiness Division.

Fig. 1-8

Unlike car maintenance periods which are only recommended, the servicing schedules of aircraft must be rigidly adhered to in order to ensure maximum safety for those who fly in them. In effect these servicing periods are similar to the Ministry of Transport car tests, but instead of every year they vary in frequency and are calculated in both calendar months and flying hours. A typical figure being one month or 50 hours between servicing inspections (or checks). The time limit which occurs sooner will apply.

Following each inspection a record of the maintenance received must be placed in the aircraft log book, and in the case of those aircraft certificated in the Transport or Aerial Work Category a Certificate of Maintenance will be issued.

Authorisation Sheet

Training organisations are required to use Flight Authorisation Sheets to record details of the training flights undertaken by their aircraft, instructors and students. Normally provision is made on these sheets for entering details relating to the aircraft serviceability upon completion of each flight.

It will be the responsibility of the pilot to check any entries made on these sheets against the aircraft concerned to ensure it is serviceable prior to each flight.

EXERCISES COMPLETED	AIRCRAFT STATE	PILOTS SIGNATURE	COMMENTS
9. 12. 13.	S		NIL
16. 17(a)	u/s		NOSE OLEO FLAT

Technical Log

Aircraft in the Public Transport Category which are normally operated for the purposes of public transport will usually be equipped with a document known as a *'Technical Log'*. This document is used to record the aircraft flight times, items of unserviceability and any rectification work, which has been carried out.

Although private pilots may not engage in flight operations for the purposes of *'hire and reward'* they might from time to time fly aircraft which use Technical Logs and must therefore understand their purpose and how to use them.

Failure to Comply with Conditions or Requirements of the ANO

If the pilot at any time during flight fails to observe or acts contrary to any of the relevant conditions or requirements included in the Certificate of Airworthiness it will for that period of time be invalidated.

There are three important aspects to be considered by any pilot in relation to acting contrary to the conditions contained in the Certificate of Airworthiness:

- It may make him liable under Article 87, Schedule 13 of the ANO to a fine not exceeding £1000 and/or a term of imprisonment not exceeding two years.
- The aircraft or personal insurance poicies applicable to aircraft and pilots normally carry a clause which states that the policy will become null and void if the pilot does not abide by national or international regulations.
- The aircraft warranty will automatically become void if the aircraft is operated contrary to the manufacturers instructions or limitations.

It can therefore be seen that ignorance of or deliberate contravention of the regulations pertaining to Certificates of Airworthiness could not only jeopardise flight safety, but also place the pilot in a position where punitive action could be taken against him and if involved in an accident whilst he was in breach of the regulations severe financial penalites could result.

Issue and Renewal of Certificate of Airworthiness
Validity Periods (Calendar Time)

Certificates of Airworthiness have a validity period of three years when issued for the Transport or Private Category.

If issued in the Special Category the period of validity may be for any period of time up to three years.

All validity periods relate to calendar months calculated from the date of issue, e.g. a two year C of A issued on 1.6.83 will lapse at midnight on 31.5.85.

Overhaul, Repair, Replacement and Modification to Aircraft or Equipment

If at any time during the period of validity the aircraft or any equipment required for its airworthiness is overhauled, repaired, removed, replaced or modified, a Certificate of Compliance must be issued by a qualified aircraft engineer. There are however certain occasions when exceptions to this regulation may be made and these are covered in Manual 3 Section 7 which relates to *"Airworthiness, Certification and Maintenance"*.

```
CERTIFICATE of COMPLIANCE

I hereby certify that the inspection/overhaul/repair/
replacement/modification specified above has been
carried out in accordance with the requirements of
Chapter A4-3 of British Civil Airworthiness Require-
ments.

          Signed....................
          Firm.....................
          CAA Approval Ref.
          or Licence No............
          Date.....................
```

Equipment of Aircraft

Apart from the equipment which is considered necessary to ensure the airworthiness state of the aircraft, certain additional equipment may be required depending upon the type of operation, e.g. flights for the purposes of public transport or private operations and whether it is being used by day or by night and operating over land or water etc.

Equipment Required in Relation to the Circumstances of Flight
To meet these varying circumstances and to ensure that the requisite level of flight safety is maintained during different types of flight operation the ANO sets out a table of equipment which is considered to be an essential minimum to fit these purposes. Fig. 1-9 shows an extract from this table.

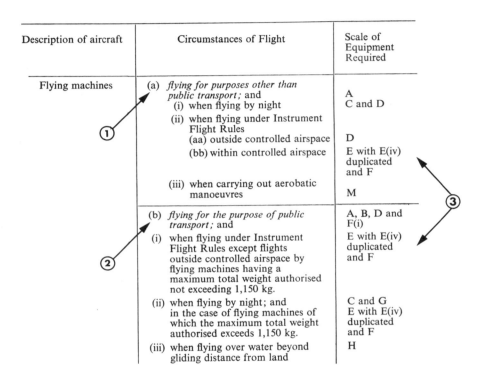

Description of aircraft	Circumstances of Flight	Scale of Equipment Required
Flying machines	(a) *flying for purposes other than public transport;* and	A
	(i) when flying by night	C and D
	(ii) when flying under Instrument Flight Rules	
	(aa) outside controlled airspace	D
	(bb) within controlled airspace	E with E(iv) duplicated and F
	(iii) when carrying out aerobatic manoeuvres	M
	(b) *flying for the purpose of public transport;* and	A, B, D and F(i)
	(i) when flying under Instrument Flight Rules except flights outside controlled airspace by flying machines having a maximum total weight authorised not exceeding 1,150 kg.	E with E(iv) duplicated and F
	(ii) when flying by night; and in the case of flying machines of which the maximum total weight authorised exceeds 1,150 kg.	C and G E with E(iv) duplicated and F
	(iii) when flying over water beyond gliding distance from land	H

Fig. 1-9

Where a charge is made for the use of the aircraft owned by a training organisation, the aircraft will normally be equipped to meet the requirements of public transport operation. Figure 1-9 shows the scales required for *'other than public transport purposes'* as well as some of the equipment requirements when the aircraft is being used for the *'purpose of public transport'*, see items 1 & 2.

The equipment indicated by the scales A, B, C, D etc. (ref item 3 of Fig. 1-9) are defined in detail in a section of the ANO which follows the table and as an example of this, Fig. 1-10 illustrates part of the contents of Scale A, and the total contents of Scales C, D and E.

Note: Due to the changes which are made from time to time in relation to aircraft equipment requirements it will be necessary to refer to the ANO (as amended) in order to determine current equipment requirements.

Scale A

(i) Spare fuses for all electrical circuits the fuses of which can be replaced in flight, consisting of 10 per cent. of the number of each rating or three of each rating, whichever is the greater;

(ii) Maps, charts, codes and other documents and navigational equipment necessary, in addition to any other equipment required under this Order, for the intended flight of the aircraft, including any diversion which may reasonably be expected.
:::::::   :::::::   :::::::   ::::

Scale C

(i) Equipment for displaying the lights required by the Rules of the Air and Air Traffic Control;

(ii) Electrical equipment, supplied from the main source of supply in the aircraft, to provide sufficient illumination to enable the flight crew properly to carry out their duties during flight;

(iii) Unless the aircraft is equipped with radio, devices for making the visual signal specified in the Rules of the Air and Air Traffic Control as indicating a request for permision to land.

Scale D

(i) Either (a) a turn indicator and a slip indicator; or
         (b) a gyroscopic bank and pitch indicator and a gyroscopic direction indicator;

(ii) A sensitive pressure altimeter adjustable for changes in barometric pressure.

Scale E

(i) A turn indicator and a slip indicator;

(ii) A gyroscopic bank and pitch indicator;

(iii) A gyroscopic direction indicator;

(iv) A sensitive pressure altimeter adjustable for changes in barometric pressure;

Provided that any aircraft may, at the option of the operator, be equipped with an additional gyroscopic bank and pitch indicator in lieu of the turn indicator referred to in (i) of this Scale.

Fig. 1-10

Radio Equipment of Aircraft

The need to carry radio equipment is not applicable to all flights, however there are occasions when radio will be required, e.g. when taking off or landing at busy aerodromes, whilst traversing the airspace surrounding such aerodromes and on certain other occasions.

Although the requirements to carry radio for public transport operations are fairly stringent, the carriage of radio will only be mandatory for private or training flights if such flights are made are very high altitudes or in the vicinity of certain airfields which are surrounded by some form of Controlled Airspace.

The UK airspace, as is the case in most countries, is basically divided into two sections, Controlled and Uncontrolled Airspace. The various types of controlled airspace are known as Terminal Areas, Control Zones and the Airways which form corridors between major airports. Additionally at some smaller but busy aerodromes Special Rules Zones and Special Rules Areas may exist.

When a flight for any purpose has to be routed into any of these types of controlled or special airspace, certain regulations regarding the carriage of radio will have to be complied with. Schedule 6 of the ANO describes the circumstances in which the various scales of radio equipment must be carried, and part of this schedule is shown on the next page at Fig. 1-11.

Radio Equipment to be carried in Aircraft

Every aircraft shall be provided, when flying in the circumstances specified in the first column of the table below, with the scales of equipment respectively indicated. Provided that, if the aircraft is flying in a combination of such circumstances the scales of equipment shall not on that account be required to be duplicated.

Table

Aircraft and Circumstances of Flight	A	B	C	D	E	F	G
1. All aircraft within the United Kingdom:							
(a) when flying under Instrument Flight Rules within controlled airspace.	A					F*	
(b) where required by regulations made under the ANO to comply in whole or in part with Instrument Flight Rules in Visual Meteorological Conditions.	A*				E*	F*	
(c) when flying within any airspace in respect of which special rules are prescribed by the said regulations in relation to a particular aerodrome, so as to require two-way radio communication with that aerodrome.	A*						
(d) when making an approach to landing at an aerodrome notified for the purpose of this sub-paragraph.							G*
2. All aircraft (other than gliders) within the United Kingdom when flying at or above flight level 245.	A*				E*	F*	

*Unless the appropriate air traffic control unit otherwise permits in relation to the particular flight and provided that the aircraft complies with any instructions which the air traffic control unit may give in the particular case.

Fig. 1-11

Some example of scales of radio equipment in relation to the above table are:

Scale	Equipment
A	Two Way Radio Communication Equipment
B	Radio Navigation Equipment
E	Transponder (Radar Interrogation Equipment)
F	DME (Distance Measuring Equipment)
G	ILS (Instrument Landing System Equipment)

All fixed radio installations in aircraft have to be approved by the Airworthiness Division of the CAA. When the installation meets the CAA requirements a '*Certificate of Approval of Aircraft Radio Installation*' will be issued and form part of the aircraft's normal documentation. A specimen certificate is shown at Fig. 1-12.

Civil Aviation Authority

AIRWORTHINESS DIVISION   BRABAZON HOUSE   REDHILL   SURREY

Certificate of Approval of Aircraft Radio Installation

Ref: RAD/GBDSL   Date 12th March 1977

Registration Marks GBDSL

Type   Cessna FRA150M

NOTE: (i) This certificate supersedes certificate dated ... N/A

       (ii) Both operator's copies of this certificate must be
            passed to subsequent operators.

ISSUE:

The above named aircraft's radio apparatus, details of which are
listed below, has been inspected by the CAA and its installation
is approved as complying with all relevant requirements of the
British Civil Airworthiness Requirements.

ARC528E   VHF Communication ILS Localiser & VOR

Fig. 1-12

HOME OFFICE
UNITED KINGDOM
OF GREAT BRITAIN AND NORTHERN IRELAND.
THE CHANNEL ISLANDS AND THE ISLE OF MAN
WIRELESS TELEGRAPHY ACT. 1949
AIRCRAFT LICENCE

Date of Issue   1 January 1977   For on issue   £4.00
Renewable   1 January in each year For on renewal £4.00

Nationality & Registration Mark of Aircraft   G-ZZZZ
Make & Type Number of Aircraft   Cessna FRA 172 M
Description of Station
Call sign of Station   GZZZZ

Further to this, an aircraft radio licence will be required under the Wireless Telegraphy Act 1949, and this licence should be kept with the aircraft documentation so that the pilot can ascertain its existence and validity. See Fig. 1-13.

R B Smith and Company
High Street, Oldtown, Anyshire.

Fig. 1-13

United Kingdom Civil Aviation Authority
FLIGHT RADIO-TELEPHONY OPERATOR'S LICENCE

M.E. Hertz   4321
                          Licence No.

is authorised to operate, in accordance with the Air Navigation Order for the time being in force, radio telephony apparatus on board any aircraft registered in the United Kingdom in the capacity of a Flight Radio-Telephony Operator (Restricted).

This Licence is valid for the same period as the Licence the number of which is shown below.

Signature of
Issuing Officer   Dated and
FCL1/9   Stamp

                    VHF only

Limitations
The holder of this Licence shall be entitled to operate radio-telephony apparatus in any aircraft if the stability of the frequency radiated by the transmitter is maintained automatically but shall not be entitled to adjust its frequency except by the use of external switching devices.

The holder of this Licence is not permitted to operate an aircraft radio station for the purpose of public correspondence.

Signature of Holder

Private Pilot's Licence No.   PP00001

Fig. 1-14

Apart from the need to have a licence in respect of the aircraft radio, a pilot will need to obtain a personal licence which permits him to legally operate the radio telephony equipment in an aircraft.

The minimum class of personal radio licence is called a '*Flight Radiotelephony Operator's (Restricted) Licence*' and pilot's must pass a written and practical test in radiotelephony (RTF) procedures before being issued with this licence. See Fig. 1-14.

Although it is illegal for a qualified pilot to operate an aircraft radio without such a licence the ANO does provide a dispensation for student pilots under training to operate aircraft radio without holding an RTF licence.

This is arranged through the flying training organisation holding the aircraft radio licence and who can give a student pilot authorisation to operate the radio station in the aircraft. This authority can only be granted to student pilots.

> *"Upon obtaining your Private Pilot's Licence you will need to obtain a Radiotelephony Licence if you wish to continue to use the added safety benefits and the wider utilisation of privileges which are available to you when an aircraft is equipped with radio."*

Facilities for training and examining candidates for the Radiotelephony (Restricted) Licence are available at most airfields where flying training is conducted.

Aircraft, Engine and Propeller Log Books

In order to maintain a record of any repairs, changes or modifications to the aircraft or its fixed equipment the following log books must be maintained by the aircraft owner or operator:

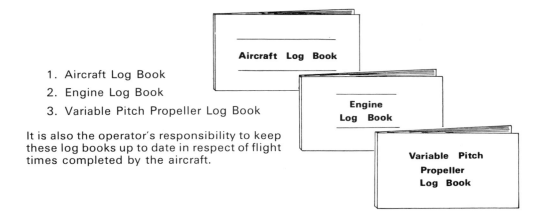

1. Aircraft Log Book
2. Engine Log Book
3. Variable Pitch Propeller Log Book

It is also the operator's responsibility to keep these log books up to date in respect of flight times completed by the aircraft.

Note: When an aircraft is equipped with more than one engine a separate log book must be maintained for each engine and when applicable each variable pitch propeller.

These log books must be preserved by the operator or owner of the aircraft until a date two years after the aircraft, engine or variable pitch propeller, as the case may be, has been destroyed or has been permanently withdrawn from use.

Such records will enable the licensed engineer or maintenance organisation to determine what work has been accomplished and to verify that the requirements of the approved maintenance schedule (or any mandatory modifications which may become necessary) have been complied with.

Aircraft Weight Schedule

All aeroplanes for which a Certificate of Airworthiness is issued must be weighed and have the position of the Centre of Gravity determined. This procedure will be required prior to the initial issue of a C of A and also on such other occasions as may be requested by the CAA.

The basic weight of an aircraft consists of the weight of the empty aircraft, together with the weight of unusable fuel and oil. It also includes the fixed items of equipment which are listed on the weight schedule.

A weight schedule must be preserved for a minimum period of six months following the next occasion on which the aircraft is weighed. An example of a typical Weight Schedule is shown at Fig. 1-15 and detailed information on calculating weight and balance is given in Manual 3 Section 5 which covers *Principles of Flight*.

EXAMPLE OF A WEIGHT AND CENTRE OF GRAVITY SCHEDULE

Reference : BA/123.
Produced by : Balanced Aircraft Ltd.
Aircraft Designation : Pivot 00.
Nationality and Registration Marks : G-BZZZ.
Constructor : General Aviation.
Constructor's Serial Number : 432L.
Maximum Authorised Weight : 758 kg (1690 lb)
Centre of Gravity Limits : Refer to Flight Manual reference No AV50

PART A BASIC WEIGHT
The basic weight of the aircraft as calculated from the weighing report supplied by General Aviation reference W/Bal. 00. dated 27 March 1975 is : 1190 lb.

The Centre of Gravity of the aircraft in the same condition at this weight with landing gear extended is : 35.5 in. aft of datum.
The Total Moment about the datum in this condition is : 42245.0

Note: The datum is at fuselage station 0.0 and is situated at the front face of the firewall. This is the datum defined in the Flight Manual. All lever arms are distances in inches aft of datum.

The basic weight includes the weight of 21 lb unusable fuel and total oil and the weight of items as indicated on the attached Basic Equipment List (not included in this example).

PART B VARIABLE LOAD
The weight and lever ... e variable load depends upon th ... ... role.

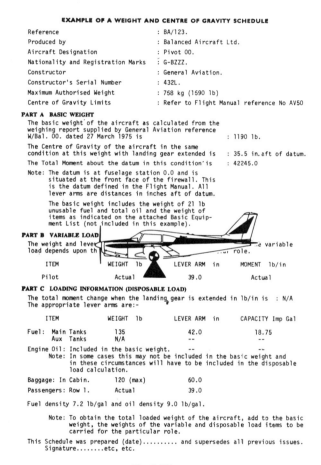

ITEM	WEIGHT lb	LEVER ARM in	MOMENT lb/in
Pilot	Actual	39.0	Actual

PART C LOADING INFORMATION (DISPOSABLE LOAD)
The total moment change when the landing gear is extended in lb/in is : N/A
The appropriate lever arms are:-

ITEM	WEIGHT lb	LEVER ARM in	CAPACITY Imp Gal
Fuel: Main Tanks	135	42.0	18.75
Aux Tanks	N/A	--	--
Engine Oil: Included in the basic weight.	--	--	--

Note: In some cases this may not be included in the basic weight and in these circumstances will have to be included in the disposable load calculation.

Baggage: In Cabin.	120 (max)	60.0	
Passengers: Row 1.	Actual	39.0	

Fuel density 7.2 lb/gal and oil density 9.0 lb/gal.

Note: To obtain the total loaded weight of the aircraft, add to the basic weight, the weights of the variable and disposable load items to be carried for the particular role.

This Schedule was prepared (date).......... and supersedes all previous issues.
Signature........etc, etc.

Fig. 1-15

Grant and Renewal of Licences to Members of Flight Crew

This section of the Air Navigation Order covers the requirements and methods of issue and renewal of licences to all classes of flight crew. However, the private pilot need only concern himself with those particulars which concern the issue and renewal of the Private Pilot's Licence and associated Ratings.

Licences will be issued by the CAA subject to certain conditions being met in relation to the applicants medical fitness, flight experience and to flight test and examination requirements. The minimum age for the issue of a Private Pilot's Licence or the award of a Student Pilot's privileges is 17 years.

1-17

The Student Pilot's Privileges and The Private Pilot's Licence

A student pilot's privileges are limited to being able to fly 'In Command' of an aircraft for the purposes of obtaining the necessary flight experience for the issue of a pilot's licence. Such flying must be carried out under the direct authorisation and supervision of a qualified flying instructor.

Student Pilot Privileges

In order to obtain the privileges of a student pilot the applicant will be required to undergo an examination by a doctor who has been specifically authorised by the CAA and obtain an appropriate medical certificate.

A large number of such doctors are geographically distributed throughout the British Isles and your training organisation or the CAA will be able to direct you to your nearest authorised medical examiner.

The required physical standards laid down by the CAA have to be sufficiently stringent to ensure that the applicant has no physical defects which would interfere with his ability to fly an aircraft safely. However the standards are not exacting and the number of persons who are unable to meet them is relatively small.

Medical Certificates

There are three classes of medical certificates, depending upon whether the holder is a commercial pilot, commerical flight crew member or a private pilot. A Class 3 medical certificate is required to qualify for the privileges of a Student Pilot or a Private Pilot Licence. When the holder is under 40 years of age the certificate will last for a period of 24 months and when aged 40 years or over the certificate will last for 12 months.

In either case the remainder of the month in which it expires can be counted towards the expiry date. In other words a certificate issued on the 17th September 1980 to a person below 40 years of age will expire on the 30th September 1982. An example of a Class 3 Medical Certificate is shown at Fig. 1-16.

Fig. 1-16

In certain circumstances, specialist medical examinations may be required for the initial issue or renewal of a medical certificate. For example, when a candidate is over 40 years of age an Electro Cardiograph will be required. Information of this nature will be given to the candidate by the authorised medical examiner and the date of the next special examination(s) will be shown on the certificate (see item 1 of Fig. 1-16).

Notwithstanding the existence of a valid medical certificate every pilot should be aware of his day to day physical condition and if he suffers an injury or illness he must not attempt to fly as pilot in command until he is fit and well again. In any case of doubt, the pilot is responsible for consulting with an authorised medical examiner and obtaining a clearance prior to further *in command* flights.

In relation to the above paragraph the ANO states:

1. *A person shall not be entitled to act as a member of the flight crew of an aircraft registered in the United Kingdom if he knows or has reason to believe that his physical or mental condition renders him temporarily or permanently unfit to perform such function or to act in such capacity.*

2. *Every holder of a medical certificate issued under the Articles of the ANO should inform the CAA as soon as possible if he suffers:*

   A personal injury involving incapacity to undertake his functions as a member of the flight crew, or

   Suffers any illness involving incapacity to undertake those functions throughout a period of 20 days or more;

   In the case of a woman, has reason to believe that she is pregnant.

Legislation of this nature is no more than the application of common sense which is the fundamental basis of good operating practices.

The reverse side of the Student's Medical Certificate states the privileges of a Student Pilot, these are:

Provided the holder of the certificate is 17 years or more he may act as 'pilot in command' of an aircraft for the purpose of becoming qualified for the grant or renewal of a pilot's licence or the inclusion or variation of any Rating in a pilot's licence provided that:

Such flights are within the United Kingdom, the Channel Islands or the Isle of Man;

The medical certificate is valid at the time and throughout the period of the flight;

No other person is carried in the aircraft, i.e. Solo Flight, and;

He acts in accordance with instructions given by a qualified flying instructor.

The Private Pilot's Licence

At some stage during or following his required ground and flight training a Student Pilot will have to sit and pass the ground examinations and undergo a flight test.

The ground examinations consist of three written tests of the multiple choice type in the following subjects:

1. Aviation Law
2. Navigation and Meteorology
3. Aircraft Technical (General and Type)

The latter examination 'Aircraft Technical' is one which relates directly to those subjects concerned with the operation of an aircraft and its associated systems and includes, questions on Principles of Flight, Flying Controls, Engines and Instruments etc.

The flight test is a two part examination in which the candidate will be required to demonstrate his standard of competence in handling the aircraft on the ground and during flight as well as answering oral questions relating to pre-flight preparation, and the specific aircraft type.

The ground examinations and flight test must be completed within the six months immediately preceding the date of qualifying for the grant of the licence. The licence when issued will be made up of a basic licence (or title page) a medical certificate and the aircraft Rating and any other Ratings and associated certificates to which the holder may be entitled. The basic licence page indicates the class of licence, e.g. Private Pilot Licence, and the name of the holder together with his date of birth and nationality.

AIRCRAFT RATING-AEROPLANES
The holder of this licence, is entitled to exercise its privileges either as pilot in command or as co-pilot of aeroplanes as specified below.

Landplanes   Group A
Seaplanes   Group B
Amphibians

Self Launching
Motor Gliders

Group C

The licence itself will be non-expiring but the privileges it contains will lapse unless the medical certificate is renewed at the appropriate time and the holder carries out a minimum of 5 hours of flight time during the 13 months following its issue.

REQUIREMENT AND VALIDITY OF MEDICAL CERTIFICATES

Licence	Class of Medical Certificate	Validity in months*
Airline Transport Pilot		6
Senior Commercial Pilot		6
Commercial Pilot aged 40 or over	1	6
Commercial Pilot under 40	1	12
Air Traffic Control Officer	1	12
FN, FE, FRO	1 or 2	12
Student/Private Pilot aged 40 or over	1, 2 or 3	12
Student/Private Pilot under 40	1, 2 or 3	24

* In addition to the remainder of month of issue.

PRIVILEGES OF A STUDENT PILOT

This certificate permits the holder, provided he is 17 years or more, to act as pilot in command of an aircraft for the purpose of becoming qualified for the grant or renewal of a pilot's licence or the inclusion or variation of any rating in a pilot's licence provided that —

(a) such flights are within the United Kingdom, the Channel Islands, or the Isle of Man,

(b) this Medical Certificate is valid at time of flight,

(c) no other person is carried in the aircraft;

(d) he so acts in accordance with instructions given by a person holding a pilot's licence which includes a Flying Instructor's or an assistant flying instructor's rating entitling him to give instruction in flying the type of aircraft being flown.

NOTES

1 Every holder of a Licence should securely attach the Medical Certificate to the Licence to which it applies.

2 The Renewal of the Medical Certificate can be obtained in the period commencing one calendar month before expiry. The medical examination should be performed as early in the period as possible.

3 The following special examination(s) should be completed on or before the end of the month shown.

Electrocardiogram   Chest X-ray   Audiogram

4 When arranging a medical examination always inform your examiner if any of these examinations is due to be repeated. Arrangements for their completion can be made up to 60 days prior to the physical examination.

The medical certificate can be renewed by making the necessary arrangements for a further examination from an authorised medical examiner, and the 5 hours flight experience must be certified in the holder's log book by an approved Private Pilot Licence examiner. Full details on the method of logging these 5 hours is given later under the heading of 'Licences and Ratings — Renewal'.

The privileges of the Private Pilot Licence are covered in detail in the ANO Schedule 9 and these are summarised as follows:

The holder of a Private Pilot's Licence may fly as pilot in command of an aeroplane of any of the types specified in the licence. However, he shall not fly as pilot in command of an aeroplane:

1. On a flight outside controlled airspace:
    (a) When the visibility is less than 1.5 nautical miles (nm), or
    (b) When any passenger is carried and the aeroplane is flying either above 3000' above mean sea level (amsl) in Instrument Meteorological Conditions (IMC) or when flying at or below 3000' amsl in a flight visibility of less than 3 nm.
    (c) When out of sight of the surface.
2. He shall not fly on a Special VFR flight in a control zone in a flight visibility of less than 5 nm unless a special clearance is obtained from the appropriate Air Traffic Control Unit.

3. When any passengers are carried he shall not fly as pilot in command of an aeroplane at night.

4. A private pilot must not fly an aeroplane for the purpose of public transport or aerial work and he shall not receive any remuneration for his services as a pilot.

Fig 1-17 shows a graphic illustration of these privileges with regard to weather limitations i.e. flight visibility and proximity to cloud and in relation to flights conducted with or without passengers above, at or below 3000' amsl and outside and inside controlled airspace.

BASIC PRIVATE PRIVILEGES FOR FLIGHT IN
UNCONTROLLED AIRSPACE

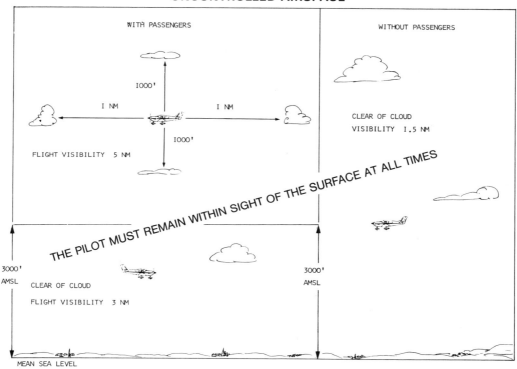

No Public Transport . . . No Remuneration . . . No Flying by Night with Passengers

Fig. 1-17

CONTROLLED AIRSPACE

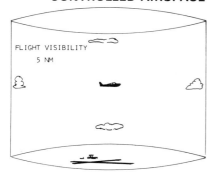

At some airfields within Control Zones there are Entry/Exit Lanes in which a private pilot may fly in weather conditions which are less than those shown in the adjacent diagram. The existence of these Entry/Exit Lanes and the procedures to follow when flying within them will be found by reference to the UK Air Pilot.

Ratings — Conditions of Issue

When a licence is first issued it will contain an Aircraft Rating card which lists the groups of aircraft the holder is entitled to fly. For private pilots the various types of aeroplanes are divided into four Groups as follows:

Group 'A' All types of single engined aeroplanes of which the maximum total weight authorised does not exceed 5700 kg.

Group 'B' Certain types of aeroplanes having two or more engines of which the maximum total weight authorised does not exceed 5700 kg.

Group 'C' Individual types of aeroplanes of which the maximum total weight authorised exceeds 5700 kg or are consiesed to be of a complex nature.

Group 'D' All types of aeroplanes which come within the definition of Microlights, i.e. Single or two seat aeroplanes having a dry (empty) weight not exceeding 150 kg, a wing loading (empty) of not more than 10 kg per square metre and a wing area of not less than 10 square metres.
NOTE: The term 'empty weight' is the weight of the aircraft without fuel, crew, passengers or cargo.

Privileges of the Rating

A licence cannot be issued without including a Certificate of Test and an Aircraft Rating for at least one of the above groups of aeroplanes. Once a group or type has been entered in an Aircraft Rating it will not normally be removed, but the entitlement to fly an aeroplane and exercise the privileges of a private pilot within the group, or of the type listed, will be dependent upon a certain minimum flight time being carried out by the holder of the licence in that group or in the case of Group 'C' in the specific type.

AIRCRAFT RATING-AEROPLANES

The holder of this licence, is entitled to exercise its privileges either as pilot in command or as co-pilot of aeroplanes as specified below.

Landplanes	Group A		
Seaplanes	Group B		
Amphibians			
Self Launching Motor Gliders			
Group C			

Additional Ratings which extend the licence privileges can be obtained by satisfactorily completing specific courses of training and passing appropriate examinations. These Ratings are:

The Night Rating This Rating permits the holder to carry passengers at night.

The IMC Rating The Instrument Meteorological Rating extends the privileges of a Private Pilot's Licence to undertake flights in conditions of reduced visibility.

The Instrument Rating This Rating gives the private pilot specific additional privileges in relation to flight in controlled airspace.

Licences and Ratings — Renewal

A Certificate of Test or Experience which is required under the ANO will only be appropriate to the privileges of the particular licence or rating.

In Relation to Description of Flight
The Air Navigation Order Schedule 9 sets out a table which shows the renewal requirements for each class of flight crew licence and a section of this table is shown on page 1-23.

Certificate of Test
Apart from the requirement to hold a current medical certificate the privileges of the Private Pilot's Licence will last for a statutory period of 13 months from the date of the initial flight test. This date will be shown on the Certificate of Test which is included in the licence.

Any subsequent Certificates of Test will be entered in the licence holder's logbook.

TABLE

Case	Class of Licence	Description of Flight	Certificate Required
A	Private Pilot's Licence (Aeroplanes)	Any Flight Within the Privileges of the Licence.	Certificate of Test or Certificate of Experience.
B	Commercial Pilot's Licence (Aeroplanes)	Carriage of Passengers on a Flight in respect of which the Holder of the Licence receives Remuneration.	Certificate of Test.
C	Commercial Pilot's Licence (Aeroplanes)	For Public Transport.	Certificate of Test.

Certificate of Experience

Following the issue of the licence the privileges can be renewed by carrying out a minimum of 5 hours flying and obtaining a stamp and a signature in the holder's log book from an authorised Private Pilot examiner. The 5 hours required may be obtained by carrying out the following:

5 hours in command, or

at least 3 hours in command plus sufficient dual flying with a qualified flying instructor to make the total up to 5 hours.

When the PPL examiner has inspected the log book and is satisfied that the flying hour requirements have been met, he will stamp and sign the log book which will then extend the holder's PPL privileges for a further 13 months.

Should the holder of the PPL fail to carry out the required 5 hours of flying during the statutory 13 months, he will have to carry out a further flight test to renew his privileges. However if the holder has not flown as pilot in command for 26 months after the expiry of the certificate of test or last certificate of experience he will have to undertake further training in the form of:

1 Hour Dual: Consisting of at least: take-offs circuits and landings, general handling manoeuvres, and one simulated forced landing.

1 Solo Flight.

A Flight Test: Consisting of general handling manoeuvres and a cross country flight of not less than 50 nm with a landing at destination and a return to the departure aerodrome.

The pilot will be examined in pre-flight planning as part of the test.

If a pilot has not flown as pilot in command for more than 4 years he will have to apply to the Licensing Section of the CAA giving details of his flight experience, licences and ratings held. the CAA will then decide upon the type and amount of training required before the candidate can apply for a test to renew his privileges.

Note: It is the personal responsibility of all pilots to ensure that their licences and privileges are valid, during any flight they undertake as pilot in command.

Personal Flying Log Book

Any person who engages in flying for the purposes of qualifying for the grant or renewal of a licence or rating, or who acts as a pilot or other member of flight crew during flight must keep a personal flying log book.

Evidence of flying time is needed when applying for a licence or a rating and also when you wish to obtain the stamp and signature to renew your certificate of experience. The ANO requires that the following particulars are shown in a pilot's log book:

Personal Details:
    The name and address of the holder.
    Particulars of the holder's licence.

Particulars of all Flights made as a Member of the Flight Crew including:
    The date, duration and places of arrival and departure of each flight.
    The type and registration marks of the aircraft.
    The capacity in which the holder acted during the flight.
    Particulars of such special conditions under which the flight was conducted, e.g. night flying or instrument flying.

Recording of Flight Tests:
    Any flight test required to be conducted for the issue or renewal of a licence or rating must be recorded in the pilot's personal log book.

There are several types of log book available for the pilot to purchase and Fig. 1-18 shows a page from the log book designed and produced by the Aircraft Owners and Pilots Association.

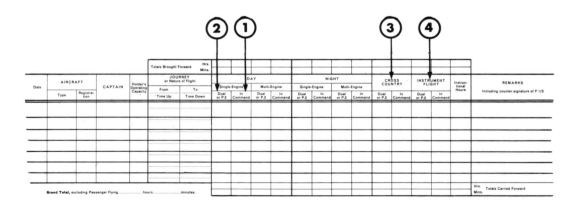

Fig. 1-18

Recording of Dual, Solo, Cross Country and Instrument Flight Times.
Log book columns are in the main self explanatory but a few points worth clarifying are as follows:

1. *'In Command'* time is that time when you are the only pilot operating the flight controls during a flight and will naturally include *'Solo'* time which is when nobody else is aboard the aeroplane. The entry made in the *'Holder's Operating Capacity'* column will be P.1. to indicate in command time.

2. When you are receiving instruction in flying you will enter the whole time spent under instruction in the *'Dual'* column and in this case the entry in the *'Holder's Operating Capacity'* column will be P.U/T.

3. Apart from a minimum amount of dual and solo flying you also need to obtain a specific number of hours on cross country flights and provision is made in the AOPA log book for these entries to be kep separately so that the current total logged can be quickly seen.

   Although cross country flight is referred to in the ANO as any flight during the course of which the aircraft is more than 3 nm. from the aerodrome of departure, the entries you will make in this column will be confined to specific navigation flights.

4. Instrument time can only be logged as that time when the pilot is flying the aircraft solely by reference to instruments.

Instructor's Endorsements of Flight Times
All log book entries should be made in ink for obvious reasons and you should also obtain your instructor's signature against all training flights to ensure corroboration of the flight time and other details.

You are also advised to take care over your entries, making them clearly legible and ensuring that the totals in the columns are added up accurately. At the end of your private pilot course and any training for subsequent ratings your Chief Flying Instructor should stamp and sign your log book before it is sent, together with an application form and appropriate fee to the CAA.

Instruction in Flying

The CAA regulations require that the student pilot is given sufficient flying training in order to attain the level of competence compatible with the privileges allowed to a private pilot.

Definition of Flying Instruction

Whenever the ANO calls for dual instruction to be given as a part of a course for a pilot licence or rating the dual instruction must be given by a qualified flying instructor who holds a current assistant or flying instructor's rating. In their own interests pilots should ensure that the flying instructor giving the dual training certifies to this effect in the pilot's personal flying log book.

Although there is no requirement for dual instruction to be undertaken in a type of aircraft which is within the Group held on the aircraft rating of a Private Pilot Licence, private pilots would be advised to obtain the services of a flying instructor for all check outs and conversion flights.

Requirement for Flying Instruction to be Given
The CAA requires a minimum amount of flying training to be carried out before issuing a Private Pilot's Licence. Part of this training must be dual with a qualified flying instructor (20 hours) and the remainder made up of solo flying (a minimum of 10 hours).

The total flying experience required is 43 hours, but certain training establishments have been granted CAA Approval to conduct and complete the course in 38 hours subject to the student reaching the required level of competence within a period of five months.

Pre-Flight Action by Commander of Aircraft

When a pilot abides by the principles of good captaincy then the requirements of safety are present. This cannot be done by just sitting in the pilot's seat and operating the controls, to achieve it the pilot will require to exercise a strong sense of personal discipline and responsibility towards his passengers and others.

This cannot begin to be demonstrated unless adequate pre-flight preparation has been carried out. The ANO broadly lays down the pre-flight actions that should be covered prior to every flight and although many of your training flights will not require all these actions to be accomplished in detail they nevertheless indicate those actions which should be reviewed prior to any flight.

The commander of an aircraft registered in the UK must satisfy himself before the aircraft takes off:

- *That the flight can safely be made, taking into account the latest information available as to the route and aerodromes to be used, the weather reports and forecasts available, and any alternative courses of action which can be adopted in case the flight cannot be completed as planned, e.g. diverting to an alternate airfield or turning back to the departure airfield.*
- *That all the equipment required for the flight (including radio if applicable) is carried and in a fit condition for use.*
- *That the aircraft is in every way fit for the intended flight, and the required documentation, e.g. Certificate of Airworthiness and Certificate of Maintenance are valid for the period of flight.*
- *That the load carried by the aircraft is so distributed and secured that it may safely be carried on the intended flight.*
- *That sufficient fuel, oil (and where applicable engine coolant) are carried and that a safe margin has been allowed for such contingencies as getting lost, or having to divert.*
- *That due regard has been observed in relation to the aircraft's performance in respect of being able to safely take off and land within the available distance at the departure and destination airfields [including selected alternate(s)] and to maintaining a safe height on the intended or alternate route.*

A pilot who before flight does not check the weather at destination and the general forecast concerning the likely weather en-route, or who does not plan for an alternate route or an alternate aerodrome (when either are available) would be acting contrary to the requirements of the ANO and the principles of good captaincy.

The same would apply if for example, a map appropriate to the route was not carried, or if a check was not made in relation to the validity of the Certificate of Airworthiness or Maintenance, or where an adequate pre-flight inspection of the aircraft has not been conducted.

With regard to the weight and balance of the aircraft used during training flights, it will often be known from past experience that the particular aircraft's actual weight is not in excess of the all-up weight authorised and that the balance will be within limits. However whenever an aircraft is going to be flown with a greater load than usual a weight and balance calculation must be undertaken.

In a similar manner, most pilots will know from their experience of operating a particular aircraft in certain conditions from known airfields, whether an adequate distance will be available for take-off or landing, but when any combination of such conditions as light winds, a heavily laden aircraft, long grass or soft surfaces and similar circumstances which will reduce aircraft performance occur, then a sensible and safe pilot will carry out performance calculations during his pre-flight preparation.

Dropping Persons or Articles

It is an offence to drop persons, animals or articles from an aircraft in flight. However this rule does not apply when an emergency situation has occurred and the commander authorises such action in order to save life or prevent damage to property, or in any of the following circumstances:

> The dropping or articles for the purpose of saving life.

> The jettisoning, in cases of emergency, of fuel or articles in the aircraft.

> The dropping of ballast in the form of fine sand or water.

> The dropping of articles for the purpose of navigation, e.g. flares etc.

> The dropping of articles for the purpose of agriculture, horticulture, forestry or public health.

> The dropping of parachutists when authority has been given to do so.

Helicopters are however allowed to lower persons, animals or articles where the Certificate of Airworthiness includes an express provision for this purpose.

Carriage of Munitions

 Due to obvious national and international implications and the dangers of inadvertent discharge of such items in an aircraft the law of the UK expressly forbids the carriage of weapons and munitions of war.

This law does not prevent the carriage of articles such as Verey Pistols or similar equipment used to discharge cartridges or flares for making the signals required by the Rules of the Air and Air Traffic Control Regulations. Nevertheless, extreme care must be exercised when handling this equipment and it must be kept unloaded unless required for immediate use.

Carriage of Dangerous Goods

In addition to munitions and weapons there are regulations which restrict the carriage of other dangerous articles unless certain stringent precautions are taken.

Dangerous goods which may be carried in reasonable safety by other forms of transportation can present extreme hazards when contained in an aircraft hold or cabin. This is due to the fact that the aircraft occupants will be unable to leave the confined space of an aircraft until it has landed.

Pilots must, therefore, learn to appreciate the potential hazards presented by certain articles which may be carried in an aircraft and goods which can be classified as dangerous for this purpose include such items as:

> Explosives of any nature.

> Flammable liquids and solids including such items as paint removers, liquid

flavouring extracts, paints and varnishes, rubber cement, alcohol, matches etc.

Oxidising materials, e.g. nitrates that yield oxygen readily, which may in turn stimulate combustion.

 Corrosive liquids, such as battery acids, certain cleaning compounds and similar agents.

Compressed gases including most household type sprays.

 Poisons, apart from the more obvious poisons this heading includes such commonplace items as pesticides.

Radio-active materials.

To appreciate the care which is necessary in determining which goods are dangerous, one has only to consider the potential effects of two very commony used household materials, fertilizer compounds and aerosol cans.

Fertilizer compounds if not packaged properly could leak or spill into an area which if dampened by moisture will produce an oxidising agent which will quietly eat into a structural component or control cable and this may not be recognised until too late.

Aerosol cans or any other item which is packaged under pressure represent a positive hazard when carried in an aircraft due to the effect of the outside air pressure lowering substantially with increase of altitude. The effect of this could result in the aerosol cannister exploding and the contents catching fire.

Another point to be borne in mind is that magnetized materials, while not inherently dangerous in the ordinary sense, must nevertheless be regarded as hazardous when carried on board an aircraft, because of their potential for adversely affecting radio navigation equipment and certain flight instruments.

With these examples in mind, it is well to remember that it is the pilot in command of an aircraft who is ultimately responsible for compliance with the regulations and the safety of any flight.

Imperilling Safety of Aircraft

"A person must not wilfully or negligently act in a manner likely to endanger an aircraft, or any person therein".

This statement from the ANO is terse and to the point, but it covers a multitude of circumstances, from a lack of pre-flight planning to such positive violations of the code of safety as deliberately flying at very low heights.

It is not intended to spell out here the manifold instances which could constitute a breach of this Article but rather to bring the regulation to the attention of all student pilots and point out that the application of simple common sense, together with a serious approach to their responsibilities as pilots, will ensure that the principle underlying this regulation is met.

Imperilling Safety of any Persons or Property

"A person shall not wilfully or negligently cause or permit an aircraft to endanger any person or property".

In a sense, this Article of the ANO is directly linked with the previous regulation. It is nevertheless spelt out in this manner to emphasise the fact that an aircraft, like a car, can be a dangerous tool in the hands of a foolhardy person, and can, if operated without care and regard for others, create hazards to the public at large and their property, whether by intent, or neglect of the pilot in command.

Drunkenness in Aircraft

"A person shall not enter any aircraft when drunk, or be drunk in any aircraft".

In relation to the consumption of alcohol and piloting an aircraft, the ANO goes on to say that no person may act as a member of the flight crew if the influence of alcohol or drugs impairs his ability.

Clearly the consumption of either, must have an effect upon a person's judgement skill and reactions, and the amount consumed and the time it was consumed in relation to the flight departure will have an important bearing upon anyone's fitness to fly.

Because of these factors and the varying effects that alcohol has on different people it is impossible to give hard and fast rules to meet every case. Pilots must understand that even small amounts of alcohol in the blood produce a measurable deterioration of performance of skilled tasks. Recent in-flight research has confirmed that even in small uncomplicated aircraft blood alcohol concentrations of 40 milligrammes per 100 millilitres (i.e. half the legal driving limit) are associated with substantial and highly significant increase in the errors committed by both inexperienced and experienced pilots. From this it is clear that even a single alcoholic drink can produce a positive loss of performance although the individual may not consider himself affected.

 It is equally important to remember that the effects of alcohol remain for a considerable time after it has been consumed. Pilots should therefore, not fly for at least eight hours after taking relatively small amounts of alcohol, while larger amounts need an even longer recovery period.

Advice on taking medicinal drugs can be considered separately in that if there is a physical or mental need for them to be taken, the person concerned must clearly be unfit to pilot an aircraft and any pilot who attempts to fly when he is medically unfit will be placing himself, his passengers and the general public at serious risk.

When a pilot enters an aircraft he becomes an integral part of a *man–machine system*, he is just as essential to a successful flight as the aircraft control surfaces. Therefore to ignore one's physical fitness during pre-flight planning would be as senseless as failure to inspect the control surfaces or any other vital part of an aircraft prior to flight.

Smoking in Aircraft

"Notices indicating when smoking is prohibited shall be exhibited in every aircraft registered in the UK so as to be visible from each passenger seat therein. A person shall not smoke in any compartment at a time when smoking is prohibited by the aircraft commander".

Whether or not it is considered safe to smoke in an aircraft is initially decided upon by the CAA Airworthiness Division and if smoking is permitted this will usually be evidenced by the siting of ashtrays in appropriate positions in the cabin. When smoking is totally prohibited in an aircraft it is a requirement to clearly exhibit *'No Smoking'* signs.

In those aircraft where smoking is permitted the ultimate decision as to when smoking can be allowed is vested in the aircraft commander who will in any event forbid smoking to take place during take-off and landing or at such other times as he thinks fit.

Authority of Commander of Aircraft

"Every person in an aircraft registered in the UK shall obey all lawful commands which the commander of that aircraft may give for the purpose of securing the safety of the aircraft and of persons or property carried therein, or the safety, efficiency or regularity or air navigation".

This authority vested in the aircraft commander must not however be abused and the basis of all such commands must relate to reasons of safety or efficiency and regularity of the flight.

Such flight begins when the aircraft first moves under its own power and the intent is to take-off until such time as the aircraft becomes stationary again, immediately prior to engine shut down.

Documents to be Carried

"An aircraft shall not fly unless it carries the documents which it is required to carry under the law of the country in which it is registered".

In relation to flights other than public transport or aerial work, e.g. private flights, there are two circumstances of flight which relate to whether or not aircraft documents must be carried in the aircraft.

Domestic Flights:
Any flight in which the aircraft departs from and lands at an aerodrome within the UK and which does not include passage over any other country is termed a *'domestic flight'* and when it is conducted for private purposes no aircraft documents need to be carried.

International Flights:
Any flight to or from any other country is termed an *'international flight'* and in these circumstances, the following documents should be carried:

★ The Certificate of Airworthiness.

★ The Certificate of Registration.

★ The Radio Licence in respect of the aircraft radio station.

★ The Licences of the members of the flight crew of the aircraft.

It will also be advisable to carry the aircraft insurance policy or a copy of this document as many countries insist upon seeing this during aircraft arrival and departure procedures.

Note: The Channel Islands and the Isle of Man are considered to be part of the UK for the purposes of this regulation.

Production of Documents and Records

"The commander of an aircraft, shall within a reasonable time after being requested to do so by an authorised person, caused to be produced to that person:

● *The Certificate of Registration and the Certificate of Airworthiness in force in respect of the aircraft.*

● *The Licences of its flight crew.*

● *Such other documents as the aircraft may be required to carry during flight under the regulations of the ANO.*

The requirements of this regulation shall be deemed to have been complied with in relation to the licences of the flight crew if they are produced at a police station in the UK within 5 days from the date of the request.

The time taken to produce such documents as are required to be kept in the aircraft or kept at an aerodrome, is considered in a different way, and is specified in the ANO as *within a reasonable time*. This is because of the practical difficulties which may arise in producing documents of this nature within a specific time.

The requirement to produce the aircraft documents when called for by an authorised person apply equally to the operator of the aircraft as well as the commander, and any member of a flight crew must also abide by this regulation in respect of his licence, rating or any certificate of validation which may be part of his licence.

Finally a similar regulation applies to the producing of personal flying log books within a reasonable time, however the pilot is not bound to produce entries made earlier than two years prior to the request.

Revocation, Suspension or Variation of Certificates, Licences or Other Documents

The Civil Aviation Authority has power to suspend, vary, or revoke any licence, certificate, or similar document which it has issued. This action can be taken pending or after any enquiry, or during consideration of the case, and in these circumstances the holder of the licence, certificate or document must surrender it to the CAA.

Whether or not a licence, certificate, or document, has been suspended varied or revoked, a breach of any condition subject to which the document was issued will result in it becoming invalid during the continuance of that breach.

Offences in relation to Documents and Records

The Air Navigation Order states:

1. *A person shall not with intent to deceive –*

    (a) *Use any certificate, licence, approval, permission, exemption or other document issued or having effect or required by or under this Order which has been forged, altered, revoked, or suspended, or to which he is not entitled; or*

    (b) *lend any certificate, licence, approval, permission, exemption or other document issued or having effect or required by or under this Order to or allow it to be used by, any other person; or*

    (c) *make any false representation for the purpose of procuring for himself or any other person the grant, issue, renewal or variation of any such certificate, licence, approval, permission or exemption or other document.*

2. *A person shall not wilfully mutilate, alter or render illegible any log book or other record required by or under this Order to be maintained or any entry made therein, or knowingly make, or procure or assist in the making of, any false entry in or material omission from any such log book or record or destroy any such log book or record during the period for which it is required under this Order to be preserved.*

3. *All entries made in writing in any log book or record referred to in paragraph 2 shall be made in ink or indelible pencil.*

4. *A person shall not wilfully or negligently make in a load sheet any entry which is incorrect in any material particular, or any material omission from such a load sheet.*

5. *A person shall not purport to issue any certificate for the purposes of this Order or the Regulations made thereunder unless he is authorised to do so under this Order.*

6. *A person shall not issue any such certificate as aforesaid unless he has satisfied himself that all statements in the certificate are correct.*

Aerodromes, Instruction in Flying

The Article in the ANO which relates to aerodromes and the giving of flying instruction can be summed up by stating that *"any of the instructional flying of the type necessary for a person to receive a licence or rating must be conducted from a licensed aerodrome"*.

Instruction in flying may also be conducted at a Government Aerodrome (Military Aerodrome) or one owned or managed by the CAA, provided that the person in charge of the aerodrome has given his permission for this flying to take place.

Power to Prevent Aircraft Flying

If it appears to the CAA or to any authorised person that an aircraft is intended or likely to be flown:

> *"In such circumstances that the flight would be in contravention of any provision of the ANO or any regulations made thereunder and be a cause of danger to any person or property whether or not in the aircraft, the CAA or that authorised person may direct the operator or the commander of the aircraft that he is not to permit the aircraft to make the particular flight or any other flight of such description as may be specified in the direction, until the direction has been revoked by the CAA or by an authorised person, and the CAA or that authorised person may take such steps as are necessary to detain the aircraft"*.

In order to determine whether the intended flight will be in contravention of the ANO or any regulation made thereunder, a representative of the CAA or any authorised person may enter upon and inspect the aircraft.

Student's Notes

Student's Notes

Student's Notes

Student's Notes

Student's Notes

Student's Notes

Student's Notes

Section 2

AVIATION LAW, FLIGHT RULES AND PROCEDURES

AIR TRAFFIC RULES AND SERVICES

GROUND INSTRUCTION

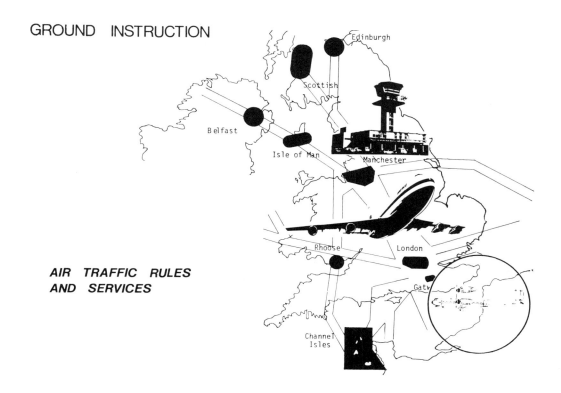

AIR TRAFFIC RULES AND SERVICES

Introduction

During the early years of aviation the safe passage of aeroplanes depended upon pilots armed with a simple set of rules of the air and a navigation chart which covered the intended route to be flown.

These operations were normally conducted in reasonable good weather and in conditions where the pilot could '*See and Avoid*'. Letting down through cloud to accomplish a landing was generally considered an unsafe procedure due to the lack of any aids other than that provided by outside visual references.

Therefore in the main, aviation safety was achieved due to limitations placed upon pilots through the lack of navigation and landing aids, and the slow speed of their machines. These low speeds, incidentally applied to most aircraft of that period whether they were small trainers or larger passenger carrying aircraft.

In more recent years the scene has changed completely and today we have considerable numbers of aircraft operating in the skies above most countries. Further to this there has been a notable change in the relative sizes, speed and performance of aircraft. Small and slow two seat trainers now have to co-exist in the same environment as very large high performance airliners and military aircraft, having performance capabilities which permit them to travel at very high speeds and in some cases well above the speed of sound.

Sophisticated technology has also entered the scene, for example, the electronic navigation and instrument let-down equipment now carried by both small and large aircraft alike has reduced the occasions when aircraft have to stay on the ground because of low cloud and poor visibility.

Because of these various changes over the years and in order to separate different classes of aircraft in the interests of safety, the sky over most countries has been gradually divided up, both horizontally and vertically into different types of airspace with varying sets of rules.

Together with this subdivision of the airspace, has grown a larger number of rules, regulations and operating procedures not all of which will need to be understood by the private pilot. He will, however need to know the procedures and regulations which govern his own type of activity and he will also need to understand that there are areas of the airspace system into which he is not allowed to go unless he acquires additional ratings and privileges.

The regulations governing the movement of aircraft at aerodromes and in flight are laid down partly in the Air Navigation Order, and in greater detail in the statutory document entitled '*The Rules of the Air and Air Traffic Control Regulations*'.

STATUTORY INSTRUMENTS

1981 No. 34

CIVIL AVIATION
The Rules of the Air and Air Traffic Control Regulations 1981

Made - - - - 12th January 1981
Coming into Operation 9th February 1981

The Secretary of State in exercise of his powers under Article 61(1) of the Air Navigation Order 1980(a) (hereinafter referred to as "the Order"), and of all other powers enabling him in that behalf, hereby makes the following Regulations—

1. These Regulations may be cited as the Rules of the Air and Air Traffic Control Regulations 1980, and shall come into operation on 9th February 1981.

2. The Rules set forth in the Schedule hereto are hereby prescribed as the Rules of the Air and Air Traffic Control.

3.—(1) Subject to the following provisions of this Regulation, the following Regulations are hereby revoked, that is to say—
The Rules of the Air and Air Traffic Control Regulations 1976(b);
The Rules of the Air and Air Traffic Control (Amendment) Regulations 1977(c);
The Rules of the Air and Air Traffic Control (Second Amendment) Regulations 1978(d);
The Rules of the Air and Air Traffic Control (Third Amendment) Regulations 1978(e);
The Rules of the Air and Air Traffic Control (Fourth Amendment) Regulations 1978(f);
The Rules of the Air and Air Traffic Control (Fifth Amendment) Regulations 1979(g).

(2) (a) These Regulations shall apply to or in relation to any licence or other document issued or granted under any Regulation revoked by these Regulations as they apply to a licence or other document issued or granted under these Regulations.

Fig. 2-1

This document is amended from time to time and at periodic intervals a new edition is issued. The copy shown at Fig. 2-1 for example, relates to the regulations which came into operation in 1976.

The contents of *The Rules of the Air and Air Traffic Control Regulations*' are divided into eleven sections which are fairly wide ranging and cover the following aspects and procedures:

Section I
Interpretation (Definitions).

Section II
Application of Rules to Aircraft.
Misuse of Signals and Markings.
Reporting Hazardous Conditions.
Low Flying
Simulated Instrument Flight.
Practice Instrument Approaches

Section III
Lights and Other Signals to be shown or made by aircraft.

Section IV
General Flight Rules:
Weather Reports and Forecasts.
Rules for Avoiding Aerial Collisions.
Aerobatic Manoeuvres.
Right Hand Traffic Rule.
Notification of Arrival.
Flight in 'Notified' Airspace.
Choice of VFR or IFR.

Section V
Visual Flight Rules:
Outside Controlled Airspace.
Within Controlled Airspace.

Section VI
Instrument Flight Rules:
Outside Controlled Airspace.
Within Controlled Airspace.
Minimum Height to Fly.
Quadrantal and Semi-Circular Rule.
Flight Plans and Air Traffic Control
  Clearances.
Position Reports.

Section VII
Aerodrome Traffic Rules:
Visual Signals.
Access to, and Movement on the
  Manoeuvring Area.
Right of Way Rule.
Dropping of Glider Tow Ropes.
Aerodromes Without ATC Units.
Aerodromes With ATC Units.
Special Rules for Certain Aerodromes.

Section VIII
Special Rules for Low Level Cross-Channel Traffic.

Section IX
Special Rules for Air Traffic in the Upper Flight Information Regions.

Section X
Aerodrome Signals and Markings.
Distress, Urgency and Safety Signals.

Section XI
Air Traffic Control.

Reference to these rules is made from time to time in the following pages and some detailed extracts are included at the end of this section.

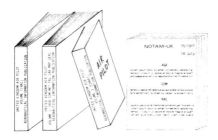

Additional detailed information in relation to Air Traffic Rules, Services and Procedures to be adopted during flight operations in the different types of airspace and at particular aerodromes, is contained in the UK Air Pilot and Notices to Airmen (NOTAMS). These documents are explained later in this section.

The following pages contain a general explanation of the UK airspace system, and the important items relating to operations within it. It should however be noted that legislation in relation to aircraft operations is not always of an inflexible nature and upon certain occasions and in certain circumstances exemptions are given from the rules laid down. To obtain further information in relation to exemptions and dispensations it will be necessary to refer to the appropriate statutory document for details of the procedures to be followed.

Division of Airspace in the United Kingdom

The airspace above the UK and the surrounding waters is divided into two large areas known as '*Flight Information Regions*' (FIR's). They are the London FIR, and the Scottish FIR. Figure 2-2 shows these regions in plan view together with the names of the adjacent Continental FIR's.

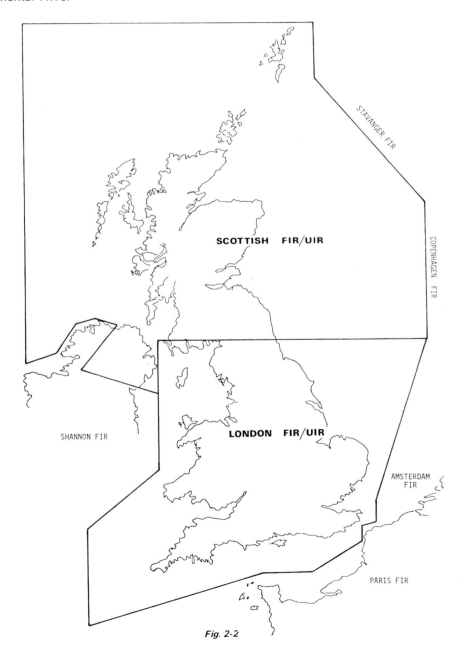

Fig. 2-2

The London and Scottish FIR's extend upwards from mean sea level to approximately 24,500 feet. Above this level and covering the same geographic areas there are two Upper Information Regions (UIR's) and within them additional rules apply, e.g. within this airspace it is mandatory for aircraft to carry radio equipment unless otherwise authorised.

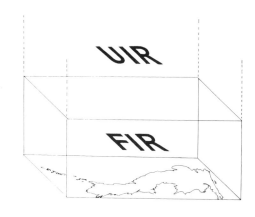

Such airspace is *'notified'* for this purpose and Article 14 and Schedule 6 of the ANO refers to this requirement (see paragraph 2 of the Table illustrated on page 1-14).

Certain parts of the FIR's and UIR's have been classified as *'Controlled Airspace'*, *'Advisory Airspace'*, *'Special Rules Airspace'*, *'Aerodrome Traffic Zones'* and *'Military Aerodrome Traffic Zones'*.

Controlled Airspace
Controlled airspace is further subdivided into three types of areas, *'Control Zones'* (CTR's), *'Airways'* and *'Terminal Control Areas'* (TMA's). Figure 2-3 shows the disposition of the Control Zones existing in the UK including the Channel Islands and the Isle of Man.

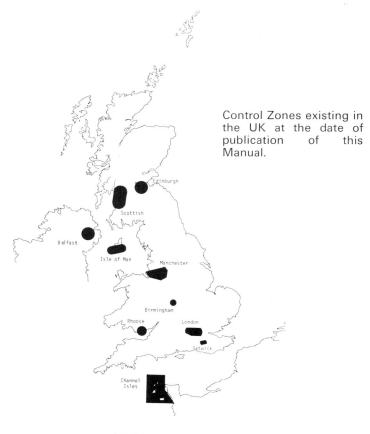

Control Zones existing in the UK at the date of publication of this Manual.

Fig. 2-3

These Control Zones are established around major airports from ground level to specific altitudes in order to give the passenger carrying airliners and other commercial air traffic added protection during flight in these areas.

This is achieved by restricting the movements of some aircraft into the airspace unless the pilot holds the additional privileges of an Instrument Rating, a qualification which is obtained by more rigorous training than that required for a basic licence.

Airways

In order to expedite and protect the flow of passenger carrying aircraft on public transport operations between major airports, Control Areas known as Airways have been established. The Airways are normally 10nm wide and extend vertically from a specific lower limit to an upper limit which is usually in the region of 25,000 feet above means sea level (amsl). Figure 2-4 shows an illustration of an Airway, and Fig. 2-6 shows how these Airways criss cross the UK.

Fig. 2-4

Those portions of Airways which are adjacent to Control Zones will often have lower bases than the en-route sections. This is to afford protection to aircraft using Airways and which are climbing up from, or descending outside the limits of the particular Control Zone. Reference Fig. 2-5.

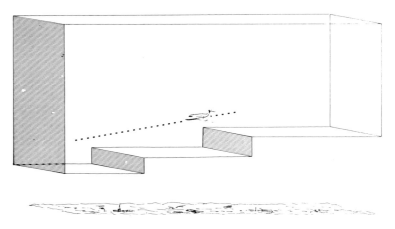

Fig. 2-5

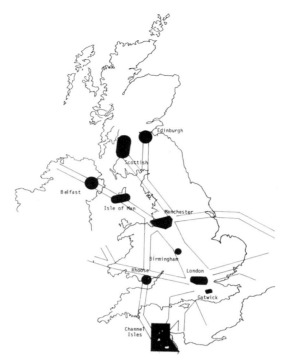

Fig. 2-6

Individual Airways are identified by a colour code and number system which is sometimes supplemented by the description, East, West, North or South, e.g. Red One, Red One North.

Terminal Control Areas

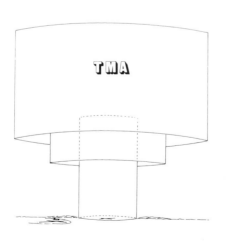

Fig. 2-7

Where Airways intersect in the vicinity of Control Zones, additional controlled airspace known as Terminal Control Areas (TMA's) are established, the geographic dimensions of which are larger than the associated Control Zones.

However it is not normally necesary for a TMA to extend down to the surface and a descriptive picture of the vertical shape which may apply to a TMA is shown at Fig. 2-7.

It will be seen that the base of the TMA is stepped up as it extends outwards from the associated Control Zone, this permits a greater area of uncontrolled airspace to exist in the lower levels and thus allows light aircraft to operate into and out of other airfields which may be situated close to a Control Zone and without having to exercise strict control over their movements.

Further to this and when circumstances permit, cut outs may be incorporated in the TMA (as shown in Fig. 2-8) to permit even greater flexibility of light aircraft movements to take place within the uncontrolled section of airspace.

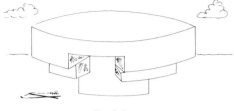

Fig. 2-8

An illustration of how TMA's are established throughout the UK is shown below in Fig. 2-9.

TMA's existing in the UK at the date of publication of this Manual.

Fig. 2-9

Advisory Airspace
Outside controlled airspace, certain Advisory Areas and Routes have been established and a specific air traffic control service is available on request to pilots who use these areas or routes. This service includes a facility to provide continuous separation from participating aircraft.

Advisory Routes are established between specific geographic locations and extend vertically from minimum to maximum cruising levels. Normally the service available within Advisory Airspace is used by a general cross section of aircraft users, e.g. private, air taxi, etc. However larger passenger carrying aircraft sometimes find it convenient to use these areas according to the dictates of the route(s) they are using.

Special Rules Airspace

Special Rules Airspace is established within the FIR's/UIR's when it is considered necessary to assist the orderly flow of air traffic. The private pilot will be mainly concerned with the Special Rules Zones (SRZ's) and Special Rules Areas (SRA's) which are established in the lower levels around certain busy airfields not protected by Control Zones. It should nevertheless be noted that some airfields which have Control Zones also have Special Rules Zones.

The basic purpose of Special Rules Zones or Areas is to afford additional safeguards to air traffic movements in the vicinity of those specified aerodromes which do not have air traffic movements of an intensity or type which would warrant the establishment of a Control Zone (together with its attendant restrictions) but for air traffic safety reasons do need added protection in the form of procedures additional to those normally considered necessary at less busy airfields.

In the broader sense these Zones and Areas can be considered as mini Control Zones and Terminal Ares in so far as their horizontal and vertical structure is concerned. For example a Special Rules Zone is an area of specified geographic dimensions around a particular airfield which extends from the surface to a specified level. A Special Rules Area has specified geographic dimensions which extend from a specified altitude above the surface with a specified top level, but this level may not be co-incident with the top of the associated SRZ.

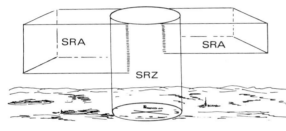

Fig. 2-10

Figure 2-10 shows how a SRZ/SRA may be constructed, but it should be noted that:

The vertical and geographic dimensions vary with the particular SRZ/SRA.

Military Aerodrome Traffic Zones

At certain military aerodromes, zones have been established to afford added protection to military air traffic departing from or arriving at those airfields. These zones known as MATZ normally comprise the airspace within 5 nm radius of the particular aerodrome and extend upwards from the surface to 3000 feet above aerodrome level.

To further protect aircraft on the final approach path of the main runway used at the airfield it is often necessary to have a projection or *'stub'* area extending some 5 nm outwards from the MATZ boundary and encompassing the area 2 nm either side of the approach path centre line. This stub area normally extends from 1000 feet above the surface to 3000 feet above the aerodrome level. Figure 2-11 shows a typical MATZ in elevation.

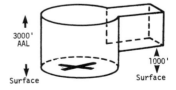

Fig. 2-11

VMC, IMC and Notification

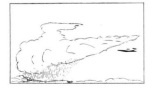

The weather governs whether or not pilots can see the ground and other aircraft in flight. Therefore it is natural for the basic regulations pertaining to aircraft operation to be based upon the weather conditions in the immediate vicinity of the aircraft.

Such weather can vary from conditions of good visibility and no cloud, to conditions of poor visibility with the aircraft close to or in cloud, hence we have two different flight conditions:

Visual Meteorological Conditions (VMC)

Instrument Meteorological Conditions (IMC)

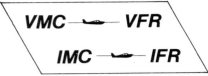

Flights conducted in VMC are carried out in accordance with the Visual Flight Rules (VFR) and those conducted in IMC must be carried out in accordance with the Instrument Flight Rules (IFR). All flights within the UK must be conducted in accordance with either Visual Flight Rules or Instrument Flight Rules.

The Visual Flight and Instrument Flight Rules are covered in the Rules of the Air and Air Traffic Control Regulations and this document defines the circumstances under which VFR or IFR can be conducted.

CONDITIONS FOR VFR FLIGHT

The basic weather conditions which relate to VMC are such that the pilot must be able to see a distance of 5 nm and remain 1000' vertically and 1 nm horizontally clear of cloud. If the prevailing weather conditions in the vicinity of the aircraft are such that the above conditions cannot be met then the flight conditions will be considered as IMC.

There are however variations from these conditions as follows:

When flying at any height in controlled airspace or above 3000' amsl in uncontrolled airspace the minimum conditions for flight under VFR are as previously stated, but if an aeroplane is operating at or below 3000' amsl the minimum weather conditions to meet the requirements for VFR are reduced as shown below.

(a) When an aeroplane is flying at a speed above 140 knots the flight visibility requirement is reduced to 3 nm but the aeroplane must still remain 1000' vertically and 1 nm horizontally clear of cloud.

(b) When any aeroplane is flying at a speed of 140 knots or below, a pilot may fly under VFR provided the visibility is not less than 1 nm and the aeroplane remains clear of cloud and in sight of the surface.

It is nevertheless important to note that the majority of UK Controlled Airspace, including all Airways, is subject to permanent IFR regardless of the actual weather conditions. A private pilot cannot enter these areas unless he holds an Instrument Rating, or unless special clearance is obtained from the appropriate Air Traffic Control Authority beforehand.

Notification to the effect that Controlled Airspace is permanently IFR is made under Rule 21 of the Rules of the Air and Air Traffic Control Regulations, and the particular airspace to which this Rule applies is promulgated in the UK Air Pilot.

It should be noted that the privileges of a Private Pilot Licence enable a pilot to fly under VFR above and below 3000' amsl. However when operating without passengers above 3000' amsl he is permitted to fly in conditions where the visibility is less than 5 nm but not less than 1 nm provided he is able to remain clear of cloud. In these latter circumstances the flight must be carried out in accordance with the Instrument Flight Rules.

Fig 2-12 illustrates the Visual Flight Rules and the requirements shown are the minimum conditions for VFR flight. However within that Controlled Airspace which is not 'Notified' as permanent IFR, it is only possible for VFR flight to take place when the flight visibility is at least 5 nm.

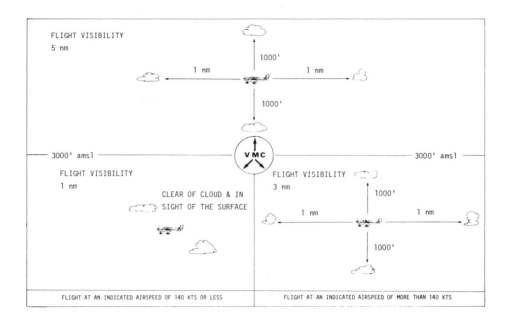

Fig. 2-12

When conducting a flight under VFR the pilot is not subject to Air Traffic Control Clearances or instructions except within Aerodrome Traffic Zones (reference 'Flight at Aerodromes' page 2-23) or Special Rules Airspace.

Therefore when conducting a flight under VFR it is entirely the pilot's responsibility to maintain an adequate lookout and a safe clearance from the ground, obstructions, other aircraft, Controlled Airspace and any hazardous areas which may be in the vicinity of his flight path.

CONDITIONS FOR IFR FLIGHT

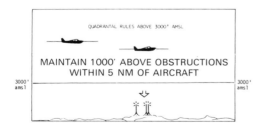

When operating outside Controlled Airspace under IFR the pilot must abide by Rules 25 and 26 of the Rules of the Air and Air Traffic Control Regulations.

Rule 25 states that 'the aircraft must not be flown at a height of less than 1000' above any obstruction which is within 5 nm of the aircraft track.

There are however a few exceptions to this rule as follows:

(a) When it is necessary for the aircraft to do so in order to take-off or land, or

(b) When the aircraft is flown along a route which is 'Notified' for the purpose of this Rule, or

(c) When the pilot is authorised to do otherwise by a competent authority,   or

(d) The aircraft is flown at an altitude not exceeding 3000 feet amsl and remains clear of cloud and in sight of the surface.

Note: In relation to (b) and (c), Control Areas in the form of TMA's and Airways are an example of routes which may be *'Notified'* for the purpose of this Rule. These normally have their bases so arranged as to ensure reasonable terrain clearance for aircraft operating within them. However sometimes an exception to this occurs in relation to obstructions, e.g. high TV masts, etc., which may result in the base of the Controlled Airspace being less than 1000 feet above such obstructions.

Pilots operating on IFR clearances within Controlled Airspace will have to use levels dictated by the existing traffic situation and as directed by ATC and this may sometimes conflict with the general princple of having 1000 feet clearance over all obstructions within 5 nm of the aircraft. Therefore to cater for this situation the above clauses (b) and (c) to Rule 25 have been established.

Rule 26 requires that aircraft operating under IFR outside Controlled Airspace and above 3000 feet amsl shall be flown at a level appropriate to their magnetic tracks, in accordance with a Table laid down by this Rule. The basis for this requirement lies in the fact that when aircraft operate in weather conditions which are less than VMC a greater risk of collision between them exists.

In order to reduce this risk standard separation rules have been established and these rules known as the Quadrantal and Semi-Circular Rule require that the aircraft altimeter be set to a standard datum of 1013 millibars (mb) and the cruising level be selected according to the magnetic track of the aircraft in relation to the Tables shown in the Rules of the Air and Air Traffic Control Regulations.

For example, when an aircraft is flying on a magnetic track which lies between 360 degrees and 089 degrees an *'odd'* cruising level must be chosen such as 3000 feet, 5000 feet etc.

Aircraft which are following magnetic tracks which lie in the reciprocal sector, i.e. between 180 to 269 degrees must fly at *'even'* cruising levels such as 4000 feet, 6000 feet etc.

Figure 2-13 illustrates this principle and it will be seen that aircraft on reciprocal tracks will have a separation of 1000 feet and those on crossing tracks a vertical separation of 500 feet. This is known as the *'Quadrantal Rule'* and it is illustrated more fully in the Table on page 2-13.

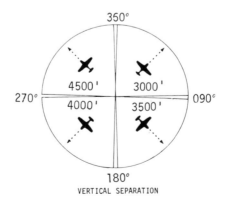

VERTICAL SEPARATION

Fig. 2-13

Above 24,000 feet the quadrantal rule no longer applies and is replaced by a second rule known as the *'Semi-Circular Rule'* as ilustrated in Table 2 on page 2-13.

QUADRANTAL RULE

Table 1   Flights at Levels between 3000 ft. and 24,500 ft.

Magnetic Tracks Degrees	Cruising Level
000 TO 089	ODD THOUSANDS OF FEET E.G. 3000ft., 5000ft., 7000ft., ETC.
090 TO 179	ODD THOUSANDS OF FEET + 500ft. E.G. 3500ft., 5500ft., 7500ft., ETC.
180 TO 269	EVEN THOUSANDS OF FEET E.G. 4000ft., 6000ft., 8000ft., ETC.
270 TO 359	EVEN THOUSANDS OF FEET + 500ft. E.G. 4500ft., 6500ft., 8500ft., ETC.

Table 2 relates to flight above 24,000ft. and although few private pilots are likely to fly at these levels there are many small multi engined aircraft which could be flown by private pilots holding a Group 'B' Rating on their licence and which can be operated in excess of this altitude. Private pilots should therefore be aware of the differences between the Quadrantal and Semi-Circular Rules.

Note: 24,500ft. is the plane of division between Table 1 and Table 2 and is not available as a cruising level.

Semi-Circular Rule

Table 2   Flights at Levels above 24,500 ft.

Magnetic Tracks Degrees	Cruising Level
000 TO 179	25,000 FEET
	27,000 FEET
	29,000 FEET
	ABOVE 29,000 FEET THE INTERVALS BETWEEN LEVELS IS INCREASED TO 4000 FEET.
180 TO 359	26,000 FEET
	28,000 FEET
	31,000 FEET
	ABOVE 31,000 FEET THE INTERVALS BETWEEN LEVELS IS INCREASED TO 4000 FEET.

Note: The above tables illustrate the principle employed in the vertical separation of aircraft during cruising flight under the Instrument Flight Rules. However it will be seen later (page 2-21) that the term *'Flight Level'* is used in place of *'altitude'* when operating in accordance with the Quadrantal or Semi-Circular Rules.

Although it is mandatory to operate at cruising levels selected in accordance with either of the foregoing tables when the flight is conducted under IFR, it is not so when flying en-route under VFR.

This is because the basic private pilot privileges only permit flight which is clear of cloud at all times. If cloud is present at or in the close vicinity of the selected cruising level and the pilot were to maintain that level he would be exceeding his privileges and breaking the law.

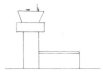

Different rules apply for flight in accordance with IFR outside and inside Controlled Airspace. Private pilots are not normally permitted to operated under IFR in Controlled Airspace unless they hold an Instrument Rating, nevertheless they are allowed to enter such airspace on certain occasions and under certain conditions.

Therefore all pilots should have an understanding of the application of Instrument Flight Rules within Controlled Airspace so that they may appreciate and anticipate the movement of IFR traffic if operating in these areas.

Aircraft operating under IFR within Controlled Airspace will be subject to Rule 25, and additionally Rules 27 and 28. Rule 27 concerns the *'Filing'* of flight plans and Rule 28 applies to the making of *'Position Reports'* additional to those normally used in the vicinity of aerodromes.

Rule 26 (the quadrantal rule) does not apply as aircraft cruising levels within Controlled Airspace will be governed by ATC clearances which are based upon achieving safe separation standards compatible with the current movements of air traffic which may be descending, climbing or in transit through these areas.

Rule 27 requires a Flight Plan to be filed, and an ATC clearance to be issued prior to entering or taking off from any point within the Controlled Airspace. The pilot must abide by the flight clearance in respect of altitudes, cruising levels and routes so that the Air Traffic Control unit knows exactly where the aircraft is at all times, and thus ensuring a safe and smooth flow of air traffic within the area.

Rule 27 will apply within Controlled Airspace regardless of whether IMC or VMC obtains, however certain relaxations may be applied to the departure and let-down phases of flight during Visual Meteorological Conditions.

Rule 28 is linked in with Rule 27 in that *'Position Reports'* must be made by the pilot in accordance with his flight clearance instructions or as otherwise directed by the relevant ATC unit.

Special VFR Flight

Those who use the airspace system have varying operational requirements and because of the nature of some flight operations, restrictions must be placed upon others in the interests of their collective safety.

However these restrictions can sometimes be relaxed without infringing their underlying principles, thus although the regulations in relation to Controlled Airspace are primarily designed to protect IFR traffic operating within these areas, certain relaxations can be made from time to time without lowering the standards of flight safety. Any relaxation of the basic regulations will however be dependent upon, the existing weather, volume of air traffic movements, and pilot competence.

Because a private pilot may not be able to operate in much of the Controlled Airspace unless he holds an Instrument Rating, the concept of *'Special VFR Flight'* has been incorporated in the regulations.

Special VFR Flight is normally only applicable to Control Zones and some Special Rules Airspace, thus permitting the private pilot access to aerodromes situated within them. It does not apply in any circumstances to Airways.

Permission for this type of flight will usually be given on those occasions when reasonably good weather exists and when air traffic movements are not too dense. However on those occasions when the visibility is less than 5 nm an Instrument Meteorological Conditions (IMC) Rating must be held by the pilot, in which case and provided circumstances allow he will be permitted to conduct Special VFR Flight down to a visibility of not less than 1.5 nm.

Note: An IMC Rating is an additional rating which can be obtained by a private pilot after he has acquired a certain number of flying hours and completed a course of training. In terms of flying hours, training and testing it is less difficult than an Instrument Rating but it carries less privileges.

Although it is not necessary to file a Flight Plan for a Special VFR Flight, a prior clearance to carry out the proposed flight must be obtained from the appropriate Air Traffic Control Unit.

It must be stressed that Special VFR Flights are concessions which can only be granted when the number of air traffic movements in relation to the existing weather conditions permit.

An authorisation to make this type of flight into a Control Zone absolves the pilot from complying with IFR and also one other Rule which relates to the minum operating height for aircraft over built up areas, i.e. a sub section of Rule 5 of the Rules of the Air and Air Traffic Control Regulations states:

"An aeroplane shall not fly over a city, town or settlement below a height of 1500 feet above the highest fixed object within 2000 feet of the aircraft".

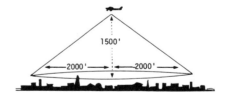

It must be appreciated that in order to maintain reasonable separation from IFR traffic, Special VFR Flight will normally be conducted in the lower levels of a Control Zone. This may therefore make it impossible for a pilot to comply with this sub section of Rule 5. The pilot however is only absolved from this Rule if the height given to him by ATC makes compliance with this 1500 ft. requirement impossible. The pilot must nevertheless operate at a height sufficient for him to glide clear of built up areas in the event of engine failure.

Throughout a Special VFR Flight the pilot will be responsible for complying with all ATC instructions and ensuring that the flight conditions, such as, forward visibility and clearance from cloud, will enable him to determine his flight path and remain clear of all all obstructions. The flight visibility should be at least 5 nm unless the pilot holds an IMC Rating.

In order to give greater flexibility to private pilot operations many aerodromes within Control Zones have Entry/Exit Lanes established to enable aircraft to operate from them in IMC without having to comply with full IMC procedures and in most cases without having to obtain ATC clearance or carry radio. These Entry/Exit Lanes are explained more fully under the heading of *'Flight in Control Zones and Terminal Areas'*.

Types of Air Traffic Service Units

Within the UK, Air Traffic Services are available in many forms and the UK Air Pilot is the main document through which these services are promulgated.

In addition to this, a service is provided in the form of Notices to Airmen (NOTAMS) which are used to inform pilots of recent or temporary changes in the services which affect the flight operations of aircraft, e.g. aerodrome runway unserviceability, withdrawal or changes in aviation facilities such as radio frequencies etc.

There are two types of NOTAM; Class I and Class II:

Class I NOTAMS contain information which has to be disseminated quickly and are therefore sent out using the Aeronautical Fixed Telecommunication Network (AFTN).

Class II NOTAMS contain information which is not of an urgent nature and are dispatched through normal postal services.

The Air Pilot is divided into three volumes which collectively have a total of nine sections:—

Volume	Section	Contents
1.	RAC	Rules of the Air and Air Traffic Services.
2.	GEN	This section covers references to the Civil Aviation Legislation and Air Navigation Regulations together with such information as the dimensional units used in flying. It also contains information on the nationality and registration marks of aircraft and the time system used in aviation reporting procedures.
	AGA	This section contains detailed information on airfields within the UK together with their hours of operation and similar details.
	COM	This section gives information on the aeronautical telecommunication system, together with details of radio facilities and frequencies for both RTF and radio navigation equipment.
	MET	This section covers the various meteorological services which are available to pilots, together with information on how to use these facilities.

FAL	This section covers such aspects as Immigration, Customs and Public Health requirements. Regulations relating to the import and export of goods, the Rules and Regulations governing the use of airfields and the fees and charges for en-route navigation services and landing charges.
SAR	This section covers the Civil Search and Rescue Organisation and the facilities and procedures which are used.
MAP	The CAA publishes a wide range of aeronautical maps and charts for the use by civil pilots. Details of these are given in this section of the Air Pilot.
3. CHARTS	This volume contains information relating to the airfield instrument approach charts which are published by the CAA.

Air Traffic Service Units (ATS) are dispersed throughout the country at various aerodromes and Control Centres. Details of the types of ATS units available and information on their facilities can be found in the UK Air Pilot Volume 1 RAC section.

Air Traffic Control Centres
These are established in the Flight Information Regions to provide air traffice services to aircraft operating within these areas. The facilities they provide are given in the Air Pilot and in summary are as follows:

Flight Information Service and Alerting Service to aircraft within the particular FIR/UIR.

Air Traffic Advisory Service to aircraft flying under IFR in Advisory Service Areas or along Advisory Routes within the particular FIR/UIR.

Area Control Service to aircraft flying under IFR in Airways and Control Areas, or under VFR in Special Rules Areas or Zones.

Area Control Service in some of the larger Control Zones within the FIR/UIR.

Zone Control Units
These are sometimes established in Control Zones to control aircraft flying within the particular Zone, but not taking off or landing. Normally Zone Control Units are established at very busy major airports to relieve the work load on controllers who handle aircraft approaching to or departing from aerodromes within that Control Zone.

Approach Control Units
These units provide,

An approach control service to aircraft taking off or landing under IFR. They may also control and integrate VFR and IFR movements.

An area service as well as an approach control function to aircraft flying within the appropriate Control Zone.

Aerodrome Control Units

These units control all aerodrome traffic which is not being handled by approach control units. They normally control all aircraft ground movements and VFR flights in the particular aerodrome circuit.

Radar Facilities

A Lower Airspace Radar Advisory Service is available to en-route aircraft. This service is provided by Radar Units at a large number of aerodromes within the UK. Figure 2-14 illustrates the geographic coverage of this particular service. It will nevertheless be necessary to consult the UK Air Pilot for up to date information regarding these facilities.

Airfields
Participating
as at 1.6.79

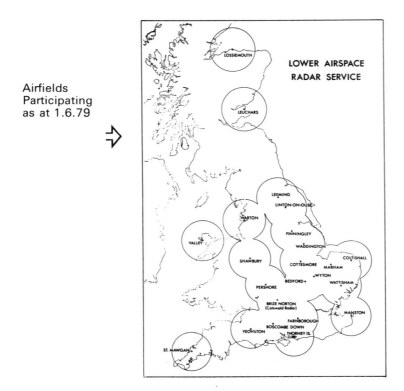

Fig. 2-14

The service is available to all aircraft flying in UK uncontrolled airspace between 3000 ft. amsl and FL80 within approximately 30 nm of each airfield participating in this scheme.

Pilots will be required to inform the radar controller on initial contact of their flight conditions, i.e. VMC or IMC, and thereafter to advise them of any change in these conditions.

There are three types of service available:

VMC Service — When the aircraft is flying in VMC, i.e. a minimum of 5 nm flight visibility and at least 1 nm horizontally and 1 000 ft. vertically from cloud. The pilot will be advised of the bearing and distance of conflicting traffic together with such avoiding action as the radar controller deems necessary to achieve a safe separation assuming the pilot does not have the traffic in sight.

IMC Service — When the aircraft is flying in IMC, advice will be passed for the necessary action to be taken by the pilot to achieve a safe separation from observed traffic.

Pilots may request IMC service irrespective of flight conditions, or such service may be instituted by the radar controller when the density or complexity of the traffic situation makes it necessary.

Emergency Service — In emergency, pilots will be given all possible assistance.

When using this radar service terrain clearance will be the responsibility of the pilot. However, when a pilot reports IMC, controllers may set a flight level based upon the standard setting of 1013.2 mb, and below which they will not provide a service.

Apart from the aerodromes shown in Fig. 2-14, many other aerodromes in the UK are equipped with radar facilities which will provide radar assistance upon request.

Altimeter Setting Procedures

In order to determine distance above the earth's surface aircraft are equipped with pressure sensitive altimeters which are calibrated in feet and operate through the pressure changes in the atmosphere.

Aircraft altimeters have an adjustable knob which permits the pilot to set a desired reference datum in millibars (units of the dyne scale). This adjustable datum facility is necessary to cater for the normal changes in atmospheric pressure at the earth's surface and for other reasons outlined in the following text.

The datums which are normally used are:
- Mean Sea Level Pressure.
- Aerodrome Surface Pressure.
- International Datum Level known as the Standard Setting of 1013 millibars (mb).

When the pressure is set to the pressure prevailing at sea level, the altimeter will indicate altitude above sea level (QNH). Whenever the QNH is set on the datum scale the term *altitude* is used.

Whenever the datum is set to the pressure existing at the surface of the particular aerodrome (QFE) the altimeter is said to be measuring *height*. An altimeter set to QFE will read zero when the aircraft is on the surface of the particular aerodrome.

Where the datum pressure used is the International Standard pressure setting, i.e. 1013.2 mb (QNE), the altimeter will indicate *'flight level'*. The pilot must understand the significance of the terms, height, altitude and flight level in order to operate his aircraft safely and fly in accordance with any instructions issued by ATC.

In relation to VFR flight and the private pilot, the QFE is normally used for take-off, landing and all flights within an aerodrome circuit. However, the earth's surface is irregular and ground level varies according to geographic location, therefore during those flights conducted away from the aerodrome it will be necessary to set the QNH value in order to assess the aircraft's clearance from the surface.

Terrain Clearance

Aeronautical maps and charts show the heights of surface contours and obstructions relative to mean sea level, therefore provided the QNH value (which relates to the mean sea level datum) is used, a pilot will be able to determine the altitude necessary to maintain a safe terrain clearance throughout the period of his flight.

Because the air pressure varies across the country with changes in the prevailing meteorological conditions the pilot will need to reset the QNH periodically in order to determine accurate terrain clearance during navigation flights. In order that a pilot can update his altimeter setting in relation to the mean sea level pressure of the geographic area he is overflying, the UK is divided into a number of Altimeter Setting Regions (ASR's) and in which an Aera QNH is forecast for every hour. This QNH is the lowest forecast pressure which could be expected for the particular area during the period of validity. Figure 2-15 shows the geographic division of ASR's in the UK at the time this manual was printed.

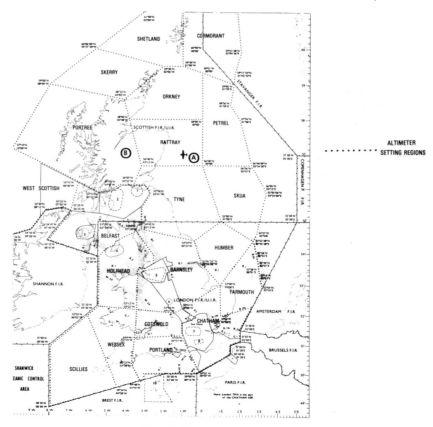

Fig 2-15

A pilot proceeding from A to B in the illustration shown at Fig 2-15 will need to contact the Flight Information Service of the particular FIR by radio in order to obtain the relevant Area QNH of the regions through which his route passes. If radio is not carried, it is possible to obtain a forecast Area QNH from the ATS unit prior to departure. Normally this forecast QNH can be obtained up to one hour ahead of the period in which it will be used.

Flight Separation
In order to ensure a safe means of flight separation between aircraft on opposing tracks in uncontrolled airspace the Quadrantal System must be used by all aircraft operating under IFR above 3000 ft. amsl.

The Standard Setting of 1013.2 mb is used as the datum for the application of both the Quadrantal and Semi-Circular Rules. When the altimeter is set to this standard datum the term *'flight level'* is used instead of *'altitude'*. The following table illustrates the relationship between flight level *'numbers'* and the altimeter indications when 1013.2 mb is set to the datum scale.

Flight Level Number	Altimeter Indication (feet)
30	3000
35	3500
40	4000
45	4500
100	10.000
150	15.000

When operating at flight levels a pilot must ensure during flight planning that the flight level(s) chosen are sufficiently high for him to maintain a safe terrain clearance en-route.

The reason for this statement lies in the fact that with the Standard datum set a pilot will not immediately be able to determine his altitude in relation to the surface below or ahead. Therefore prior to those occasions when it is intended to operate at flight levels additional care must be used to calculate a safe flight level.

To appreciate this point more fully, assume the minimum safe altitude to fly is 3000 ft. amsl and the Area QNH is 1001 mb. It must also be understood that a change in height of 30 ft. in the lower levels of the atmosphere corresponds to approximately one millibar. Referring to Fig. 2-16 a pilot using a QNH of 1001 mb will upon reaching 3000 ft. and adjusting the altimeter datum to 1013 mb increases his altimeter reading to 3360 ft. (12 x 30 = 360 ft.).

In these circumstances it would be inadvisable to use *'flight level'* 30 as a cruising level because this would place him below 3000 ft. (altitude) and in this case the lowest safe flight level would be 35.

Another term used in relation to flight levels is *'Transition Altitude'*. This is defined as the altitude in the vicinity of an aerodrome at or below which the vertical position of an aircraft is controlled by reference to altitude, i.e. with the aerodrome QNH set upon the altimeter.

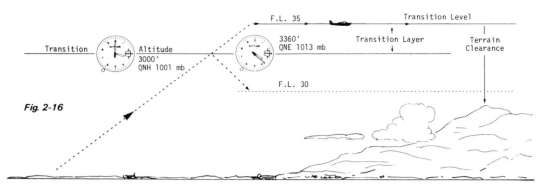

Fig. 2-16

The lowest flight level available for use above the Transition Altitude is known as the *'Transition Level'*, and the vertical distance between 3000ft. in terms of altitude and the Transition Level is known as *'Transition Layer'*. It can therefore be seen from this that the lowest flight level which can safely be used will depend upon the prevailing QNH value.

The standard Transition Altitude for civil aerodromes outside Controlled Airspace is 3000ft. on the aerodrome QNH. Aerodromes situated within Control Zones have specific Transition Altitudes laid down and these are promulgated in the UK Air Pilot.

In addition, certain military aerodromes available for civil use have a Transition Altitude above 3000ft. for terrain or operational reasons. When using such aerodromes civil pilots must conform to military procedures by setting the aerodrome QFE upon which vertical separation from military aircraft below Transition Level is based.

When operating below TMA's the pilot will have to set the altimeter datum to the QNH of any airfield below the particular TMA.

This is necessary in order to remain clear of the base of such Controlled Airspace (Ref. Fig. 2-17).

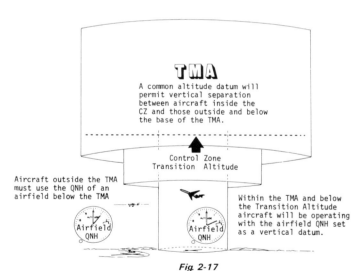

Fig. 2-17

When operating within an aerodrome circuit pattern the use of QNH or QFE is optional, however as circuit heights are quoted in relation to aerodrome level pilots will normally find it more convenient to set the aerodrome QFE prior to take-off or before descending into an aerodrome circuit pattern.

Aerodrome Circuit Pattern — Runway

Another point regarding altimeter setting procedures is that when operating within Military Air Traffic Zones whether for the purpose of transit or landing, the QFE of the particular military aerodrome should normally be used. This can be obtained by Radio from the ATC unit at the aerodrome concerned.

Flight at Aerodromes

An aerodrome is an area of land (or water) which is designed, equipped and set aside for the purpose of affording facilities for the landing and departure of aircraft.

Within the UK a large number of aerodromes are available to the private pilot. These vary from large airports which daily handle hundreds of aircraft movements,

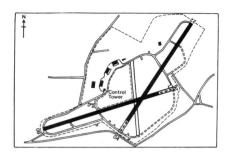

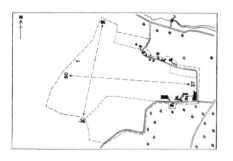

to small grass airfields where aircraft movements may be few.

Additionally a number of private landing areas in the form of grass or tarmac strips are also available, and although these may be technically considered as aerodromes they are commonly referred to as 'Landing Strips'.

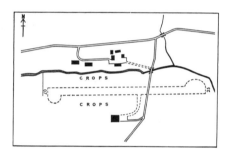

When using Landing Strips the pilot's common sense coupled with the basic Rules of the Air will largely apply, however at normal aerodromes there are specific rules which must be observed by all pilots.

The area upon which aircraft movements take place for the purposes of manoeuvring prior to and during take-off, or for landing and taxying to the parking area is designated the 'Manoeuvring Area' and on this area aircraft have the right of way over all other vehicles and persons.

All aerodromes are established with an 'Aerodrome Traffic Zone'. This is an area surrounding the aerodrome which has a horizontal radius of 1.5 nm from the aerodrome boundary and extends up to 2000 ft. above the aerodrome elevation.

When an aerodrome is not equipped with ATC facilities, particular caution must be displayed when entering the Aerodrome Traffic Zone. When an ATC unit is available it will co-ordinate aircraft movements by Radiotelephony (RTF) or where applicable by a signalling lamp or ground signals.

Aircraft movements on the Manoeuvring Area or within the Traffic Zone are controlled by ATC and pilots must comply with the directions issued by ATC unless they consider it would be unsafe to do so.

In the case of military aerodromes and of civil aerodromes licensed for private use it will be necessary to obtain permission to land from the authority of the aerodrome concerned.

Permission to use military aerodromes must be obtained prior to departure and the use of such aerodromes by civil aircraft is restricted to the normal hours of watch of the particular ATC unit and then only to aircraft on flights within the UK.

Not all military aerodromes are available for use by civil aircraft (apart from an emergency) but those which can be used are listed in the AGA section of the UK Air Pilot.

At unlicensed aerodromes, permission to land must be obtained from the owner or person in charge. The method of obtaining this permission will be either by telephone, in writing or when available by RTF. It should be noted that landing strips also fall into this category. When prior permission is a requirement to land at any aerodrome listed in the Air Pilot, it will be indicated by the annotation PPR.

Lights and Pyrotechnic Signals

When radio communication is not available between an aircraft and an aerodrome ATC unit, a system of standard light and pyrotechnic signals has been devised. The following table shows the different visual signals employed and their respective meanings when used by an ATC unit or an aircraft.

LIGHTS AND PYROTECHNIC SIGNALS

Signals From The Ground

LIGHT	FROM AERODROME CONTROL TO:	
	AIRCRAFT IN FLIGHT	AIRCRAFT ON THE GROUND
Steady Green	Cleared to Land	Cleared for Take-Off
Steady Red	Give Way to Other Aircraft and Continue Circling	Stop
Green Flashes	Return for Landing*	Cleared to Taxy or You may Move on the Manoeuvring Area
Red Flashes	Do Not Land, the Aerodrome is not Available for Landing	Move Clear of the Landing Area
White Flashes	Land at this Aerodrome and proceed to the Parking Area*	Return to the Starting Point on the Aerodrome
Red Pyrotechnic	Do Not Land, Wait for Permission	

* Clearances to Land and Taxy will be given in due course.

Signals From An Aircraft

(a) A red pyrotechnic light or flare means – 'Immediate Assistance is Requested'

⟫(b) White flashes, switching On and Off landing and/or navigation lights means – 'I am compelled to land'

⟫ *When navigation lights are being used for this signal they should be switched **ON** and **OFF** in an irregular manner to avoid confusion with those navigation light systems which automatically flash **ON** and **OFF** at short regular intervals.*

Ground signals used at Civil Airfields

The following ground signals and markings are used at civil airfields in the UK. They are either displayed in or adjacent to a part of the airfield surface known as the 'Signals Area' and which is set aside for this purpose. Some signals will nevertheless be placed on other positions of the airfield as indicated in the following text.

The signals area is usually laid out in the vicinity of the Air Traffic Control building and marked by white strips in the form of a large square which is clearly visible to pilots flying overhead.

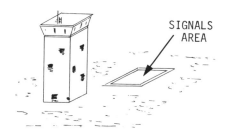

SIGNALS AREA

Prohibition of Landing:

A red square panel with a yellow strip along each diagonal signifies that the airfield is unsafe for the movement of aircraft and that landing on the airfield is prohibited.

Special Precautions:

A red square panel with a yellow strip along one diagonal signifies that the state of the manoeuvring area is poor and that pilots must exercise special care when landing.

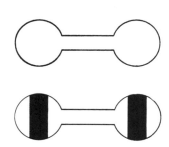

Use Hard Surfaces Only:

A white dumbell signifies that movements of aircraft and gliders on the ground shall be confined to paved, metalled or similar surfaces. The superimposition of black strips in each circular portion of the dumbell, at right angles to the shaft signifies that aircraft and gliders taking off or landing shall do so on a runway but that movement on the ground is not confined to paved, metalled or similar hard surfaces.

Right Hand Circuit:

A red and yellow striped arrow placed along two adjacent sides of the signals area and pointing in a clockwise direction signifies that a right hand circuit is in force.

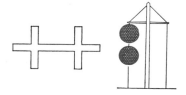

Gliding:

A double white cross and/or two red balls suspended from a mast one above the other signify that glider flying is in progress at the airfield. A yellow cross indicates the tow rope dropping area.

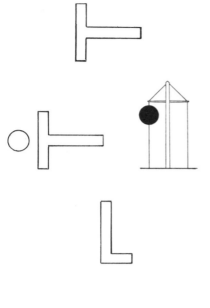

Direction of Take-Off and Landing:

A white **T** signifies that aircraft and gliders taking off or landing shall do so in a direction parallel with the shaft of the **T** and towards the cross arm, unless otherwise authorised by the appropriate air traffic control unit.

A white disc displayed alongside the cross arm of the **T** and in line with the shaft of the **T** signifies that the direction of landing and take-off do not necessarily coincide. This may also be indicated by a black ball suspended from a mast.

Landing Area for Light Aircraft:

A white letter **L** indicates a part of the manoeuvring area which shall be used only for the taking off and landing of light aircraft.

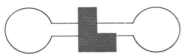

A red letter **L** displayed on the dumbell signifies that light aircraft are permitted to take-off and land either on a runway or on the area designated by a white letter **L**.

Runway Indication:

Black numerals in two figure groups, and where parallel runways are provided the letter or letters **L** (*left*), **LC** (*left centre*), **C** (*centre*), **RC** (*right centre*) and **R** (right), placed against a yellow background, indicate the direction for take-off or the runway in use.

Airfield Control in Operation:

A checkered flag or board containing 12 equal squares, coloured red and yellow alternately, signifies that aircraft may move on the manoeuvring area and apron only in accordance with the permission of the ATCU at the airfield.

Reporting Point:

A black letter **C** against a yellow background indicates the position at which a pilot can report to the ATCU or to the person in charge of the airfield.

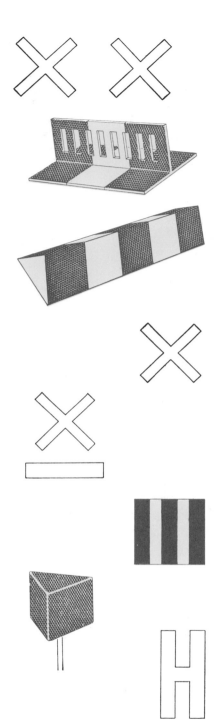

Unserviceable Portion of Runway or Taxiway:

Two or more white crosses displayed on a runway or taxiway with the arms of the crosses at an angle of 45° to the centreline of the runway or taxiway at intervals signify that the section marked by them is unfit for the movement of aircraft.

Orange and white markers as illustrated, spaced not more than 15 metres apart, signify the boundary of that part of a paved runway, taxiway or apron which is unfit for the movement of aircraft.

Unserviceable portion of Grass Areas:

An unserviceable portion of a grass maneouvring area is indicated by markers with orange and white stripes alternating with flags showing equal orange and white triangular areas.

Landing Dangerous:

A white cross displayed at the end of a runway shall indicate that landing is dangerous and that the airfield is used for storage purposes only.

Emergency Use Only:

A white cross and a single white bar displayed at the end of a runway at a disused airfield indicates that the runway is fit for emergency use. Runways so marked are not safeguarded and may be temporarily obstructed.

Land in Emergency Only:

Two vertical yellow bars on a red square on the signals area indicate that the landing areas are serviceable but the normal safety facilities are not available. Aircraft may land in emergency only.

Unserviceable Areas:

An alternative signal to mark unserviceable areas on an airfield is a solid orange triangle.

Helicopter Operations:

A white letter **H** indicates the area to be used by helicopters.

Light Aircraft:

A single red **L** shall indicate that light aircraft may land on a special grass area which is delimited by white corner markings; taxying of light aircraft on grass is permitted.

Marshalling Signals

COME AHEAD

These signals are devised to enable a form of communication to exist between the pilot and the groundcrew directing the aircraft's movement on the ground. They are laid down in detail in *"The Rules of the Air and Air Traffic Control Regulations"* and are also shown in *"The United Kingdom Air Pilot"*. Pilots must become conversant with these signals in order to control the aircraft safely when being directed and manoeuvring in parking areas.

STOP

Examples of the more common marshalling signals detailed in the Rules of the Air and Air Traffic control Regulations are shown below:

Description of Signal	Meaning of Signal	In Daylight	By Night
A circular motion of the right hand at head level, with the left arm pointing to the appropriate engine.	Start engines.		
Arm down, the palms facing outwards, then swung outwards.	Chocks away.		
Raise arm, with fist clenched, horizontally in front of the body, then extend fingers.	Release brakes.		No Equivalent Signal
Arms repeatedly moved upward and backward, beckoning onward.	Move ahead.		
Right arm down, left arm repeatedly moved upward and backward. The speed or arm movement indicates the rate of turn.	Open up starboard engine or turn to port.		

2-28

Description of Signal	Meaning of Signal	In Daylight	By Night
Left arm down, the right arm repeatedly moved upward and backward. The speed of arm movement indicates the rate of turn.	Open up port engine or turn to starboard.		
Right or left arm down, the other arm moved across body and extended to indicate position of the other marshaller.	proceed under the guidance of another marshaller.		
The right arm raised at the elbow, with the arm facing forward.	All clear. Marshalling finished.		
Arms placed above the head in a vertical position.	This bay or area for parking.		
Arms placed down, with the palms towards the ground, then moved up and down several times.	Slow down.		

Description of Signal	Meaning of Signal	In Daylight	By Night
Arms placed down, with the palms towards the ground, then either the right or left arm moved, up and down indicating that the engines on the left or right side as the case may be should be slowed down.	Slow down engines on indicated side.		
Arms repeatedly crossed above the head. The speed of arm movement indicates the urgency of the stop.	Stop.		
Raise arm and hand, with fingers extended horizontally in front of the body, then clench fist.	Engage brakes.		No Equivalent Signal
Arms extended, the palms facing inwards, then swung from the extended position inwards.	Chocks inserted.		
Either arm and hand placed level with the chest, then moved laterally with the palm downwards.	Cut engines.		

Flight Plans

Pilots intending to make a flight from an aerodrome with an ATCU must either inform ATC giving brief details of the proposed flight or file a '**Flight Plan**'. The first method is known as '*Booking Out*' and is a local procedure which is simpler than that used for filing flight plans.

However there are certain occasions when a pilot must file a flight plan and these are covered in the following paragraphs. Flight plan details are entered on a standard flight plan form (CA48) which is published by the CAA and available from the aerodrome Air Traffic Control unit. When the flight plan is completed it should be passed to ATC who will then relay the details via the Aeronautical Fixed Telecommunication Network (AFTN) to the destination aerodrome.

It is essential that the details enterd on the form are written as accurately as possible and instructions are attached to each flight plan folder to ensure that pilots can complete this action without ambiguities occurring. Flight plans must be filed with the relevant ATCU at least 30 minutes prior to requesting taxy clearance. An example of Form CA48 is shown on page 2-38.

Private pilots may, if they wish, file a flight plan for any flight but they are not mandatory for flights undertaken within uncontrolled airspace covered by the UK Flight Information Regions. Nevertheless it will be advisable to do so whenever possible if the pilot intends to fly more than 10 nm from the coast during overwater flights, or over stretches of sparsely populated or mountainous areas. This is to ensure that appropriate search and rescue action can be taken with a minimum of delay if an accident occurs away from populated regions.

A pilot is required to file a flight plan:

> For a flight conducted under Instrument Flight Rules within Controlled Airspace.
>
> For flight in certain Special Rules Zones/Areas irrespective of weather conditions. This requirement will be promulgated in the UK Air Pilot for the Special Rules Zone/Area concerned..
>
> If he wishes to take advantage of an Air Traffic Advisory Service.
>
> For any flight which crosses an International Boundary.

If for any reason a pilot who has filed a flight plan diverts or lands at any aerodrome not specified in his flight plan, it is his responsibility to ensure that the planned destination aerodrome is informed within 30 minutes of his planned ETA there.

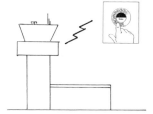

If this is not done, search and rescue action will be put into effect and cause considerable inconvenience, expense and wasted effort which might be required for an actual emergency.

Flight Information Regions and Flight Information Services

When radio is carried pilots will be able to use the *'Flight Information Service'* provided by ATCC's or Air Traffic Control Officers (ATCO's) who are based within each FIR and who listen out on specific frequencies.

These frequencies together with the appropriate call signs are promulgated in the COM section of the UK Air Pilot and Fig. 2-18 shows how this information is presented. Note that the frequency to use is dependent upon the geographic area in which the aircraft is being operated.

The information service can be used to obtain such details as Area Pressure Settings, significant weather reports, e.g. thunderstorm activity, icing conditions, fog formation, severe turbulence etc. Additionally the service can provide information relating to radio frequencies, time checks and similar items.

The Flight information Service may also provide general details relating to other aircraft movements, e.g. their headings, heights and approximate position, however as ATCO's have to rely upon pilots giving voluntary information of this nature a specific separation service between aircraft cannot be provided.

FLIGHT INFORMATION REGIONS

Scottish FIR			
East of a line 61N 06W — Stornoway — Inverness — Glasgow VOR — Prestwick along DG27 to 55N1	Scottish ATCC	133·2	Scottish Information
West of a line 61N 06W — Stornoway — Inverness — Glasgow VOR — Prestwick VOR along DG27 to 55N	Scottish ATCC	124·9	Scottish Control/ Scottish Information*2

Aircraft in the Shetlands area experiencing difficulty in communicating with Scottish FIR may call Sumburgh Approach on 123·15 MHz during its hours of opening.

Aircraft flying over the North Sea, who are unable to establish communication on 133·2 MHz may obtain FIS as follows:— North of 5730N 131·3 MHz call sign 'Scottish Control' South of 5730N 124·5 MHz call sign 'Scottish Control'.

London FIR			
South of the southern edge of Airway B1, west of the western edge of Airway A1 to the southern edge of Airway W17 then west of the western boundary of the Worthing CTA.	London ATCC	124·75	London Information
South of the southern edge of Airway B1, east of the western edge of Airway A1 to the southern edge of Airway W17 then east of the western boundary of the Worthing CTA.	London ATCC	124·6	London Information
North of southern edge of Airway Blue 1	London ATCC	134·7	London Information

UPPER INFORMATION REGIONS—SPECIAL RULES AREA (OFF-ROUTE TRAFFIC)

London UIR			
That area of the London UIR to the west of UA1E and south of UB1	London ATCC	132·6	London Control
That area of the London UIR to the east of UB4, north of UR1N and south of UB1. And that area to the north of UB1 excluding the Hebrides Upper Control Area	London ATCC	{ 131·05 { 134·25*1	London Control
Scottish UIR			
Entire Area excluding the Hebrides Upper Control Area	Scottish ATCC	135·85	Scottish Control

Not to be used for Flight Planning Purposes

Fig. 2-18

Flight in Control Zones and Terminal Areas

Private pilots who do not hold an Instrument Rating may be permitted entry to Control Zones provided reasonable weather conditions exist and IFR traffic intensity is such that VFR and IFR traffic will not conflict.

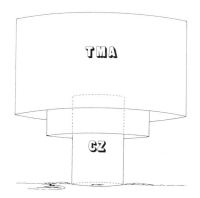

Flight in a Control Zone under the above circumstances may only take place following a specific clearance from the appropriate ATCU and it will be known as a *'Special VFR Flight'* during which the pilot must abide by ATC instructions. Normally a listening watch must be maintained on the appropriate RTF frequency but exemption from this procedure is sometimes given to non-radio aircraft.

The weather conditions governing the clearance of such flights and the heights to be flown and the routes to be followed will vary in different Control Zones. Therefore reference will have to be made to the UK Air Pilot during pre-flight planning to establish the exact procedure to use.

A *'Clearance'* for Special VFR Flight is an authorisation by ATC for a pilot to fly within a Control Zone although he is unable to comply with Instrument Flight Rules. It will only be granted following a specific request by the pilot and then only when traffic and weather conditions permit.

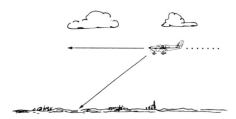

When operating on a special VFR clearance, the pilot must remain in flight conditions which enable him to determine his flight path and keep clear of obstructions. Therefore, it is implicit in all special VFR clearances that the aircraft remains clear of cloud and in sight of the surface. It may also be necessary for ATC to impose a height limitation which will require the pilot to fly either at, or not above a specific level.

A flight plan is not required for a special VFR flight but ATC must be given brief details of the intended flight, e.g. aircraft registration, aircraft type and pilot's intentions. These details may be passed either by RTF or at busy aerodromes through the Flight Clearance Office. A flight plan will have to be filed if the pilot wishes the destination aerodrome to be notified of the flight.

Requests for special VFR clearance to enter or transit a Control Zone may be made to the Zone ATC authority whilst airborne. Aircraft departing from aerodromes adjacent to a Control Zone boundary and wishing to enter the Zone, may obtain special VFR clearance prior to take-off by telephone or by RTF when airborne. In any case all such requests must specify the estimated time of arrival (ETA) for the selected entry point and when airborne this information must be passed at least 10 minutes before the aircraft reaches the Zone boundary.

ATC will provide standard separation between Special VFR Flights and between such flights and other aircraft operating under IFR, but separation cannot be given against aircraft which are using the Entry/Exit Lanes notified for certain aerodromes within Control Zones unless such aircraft are required to report their position to the Zone ATC authority. An example of these Entry/Exit Lanes is shown on the next page for the Manchester Control Zone. It should be noted that this illustration should not be used for actual flight planning purposes.

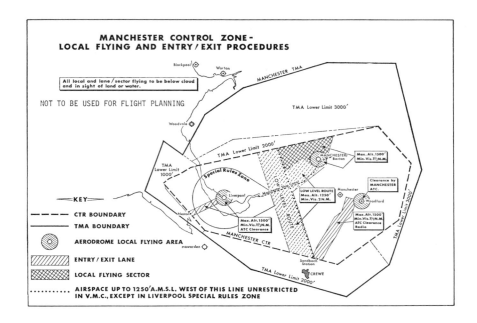

Fig. 2-19

Radio Failure

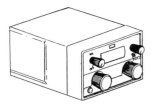

When the use of RTF is a requirement for a special VFR clearance the pilot will need to acquaint himself with the procedures to follow in the event that radio failure occurs. The actual procedure to use should radio failure occur after entering a Control Zone will vary between different Control Zones and the pilot will need to refer to the UK Air Pilot RAC Section to ascertain the exact procedure to follow.

Should a radio failure occur before reaching the selected entry point, the pilot will be unable to comply with the requirements of his clearance and he should not continue with the planned flight.

Normally special VFR flights are not permitted within TMA's as these areas do not extend down to the surface and pilots can therefore fly in the uncontrolled airspace below them.

Pilots of aircraft in transit beneath Terminal Control Areas or Special Rules Areas or departing from or arriving at aerodromes situated beneath such airspace should set the aerodrome QNH of an aerodrome within the geographic boundary of the TMA or SRA. This will enable them to determine their altitude relative to the base of the TMA or SRA. It may be assumed that any differences in QNH values for aerodromes lying within the boundaries of the same TMA or SRA are insignificant.

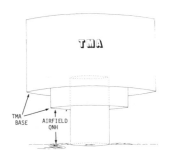

Notwithstanding the above procedure the aerodrome QFE may be used when flying within the circuit area of the aerodrome concerned.

Flight in Special Rules Zones and Areas

Pilots wishing to fly within Special Rules Zones or Areas must comply with the following procedures during the hours of watch of the appropriate aerodrome ATCU.

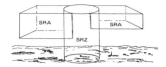

1. Prior to entering the relevant airspace, obtain the permission of the ATCU at the aerodrome upon which the Zone or Area is based and inform them, on the notified radio frequency, of the aircraft position, level and track.

2. Whilst flying within the relevant airspace, maintain a continuous watch on the notified radio frequency and comply with any instructions which the ATCU may give.

An exemption from the above requirements may be given to non-radio aircraft which remain at least 1 nm horizontally and 1000' vertically clear of cloud and in a flight visibility of not less than 5 nm and which have obtained prior permission from the ATCU.

Note: Different Special Rules Zones and Areas will have different rules and procedures and the above information represents the general rules which apply. It will therefore be necessary to consult the RAC Section of the UK Air Pilot to determine the exact procedures which exist in individual Special Rules Zones and Areas.

Flight in Airways

With the exception of certain portions which lie within TMA's or CZ's, Airways are Control Areas in which permanent Instrument Flight Rules apply and therefore they cannot be used unless the pilot holds and Instrument Rating. Nevertheless exceptions to this rule will apply to pilots wishing to cross an Airway within the UK under Visual Meteorological Conditions and in relation to aeroplanes the following procedure will apply:

1. Aircraft may, without ATC clearance fly at right angles across the base of an en-route section of an Airway where the lower limit is defined as a flight level.

    This particular exception is rather academic but it could apply in practice when a pilot is operating in VMC and on a flight level coincident with the base of the Airway concerned.

2. Pilots of powered aircraft who wish to cross an Airway in VMC, by day, may do so without compliance with full IFR requirements, in relation to aircraft equipment provided the pilot holds a current instrument rating and that prior clearance is obtained from the appropriate Airways Air Traffic Controller. This clearance must be obtained by RTF (normally via the FIR Service).

    Requests for clearance to cross an Airway and the format of the crossing report should conform to the following procedure:

    The pilot should file a flight plan with the relevant ATCU (giving details of the proposed flight) either before departure or when airborne, and request crossing clearance when at least 10 minutes flying time from the intended point of crossing.

In-flight requests should contain the following information:—

- Aircraft Identification and Aircraft Type
- Position and Heading
- Flight Level and Flight Conditions
- Place and Estimated Time of Crossing
- Desired Crossing Level

After this RTF transmission the pilot must (unless otherwise requested by ATC) remain in communication with the FIR Service and after obtaining clearance he must pass the following report when the aircraft is estimate to be entering the Airway.

- Aircraft Identification
- Airway Code Name
- Aircraft Position
- Time and Level

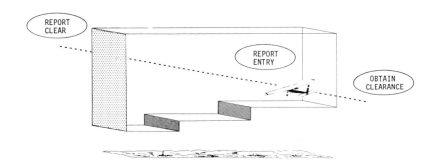

Fig. 2-20

Once the Airway has been crossed the pilot should inform the FIS as soon as possible.

Penetration of Airways without compliance with the full IFR requirements may sometimes be permitted for purposes other than just crossing. In these circumstances prior arrangements must be made with the appropriate ATCO.

Flight on Advisory Routes and in Advisory Service Areas

Outside Controlled Airspace, and within the specified Advisory Areas and Advisory Routes (ATS) an advisory service is available to all flights. In addition to the standard FIR Service, it offers a continuous separation service between all aircraft requesting this type of assistance, but not from other aircraft.

The knowledge and competence gained during a private pilot course does not equip a pilot with the qualifications and ability to use radio navigation to any large extent and therefore flight along Advisory Routes or within Advisory Areas is not covered in this manual beyond informing the student of one or two basic principles which are applicable to their use.

Participation in the use of Advisory Airspace is achieved by filing an IFR flight plan and then following certain procedures. However, as participation is not compulsory, the effectiveness of the service is determined by the extent to which pilots comply with the procedures.

It must therefore be emphasised, that even if an aircraft is flying in Advisory Airspace on an IFR flight plan and in accordance with ATC clearances, it remains the direct responsibility of the pilot to avoid collision with other aircraft not complying with these procedures, whatever the weather conditions.

Advisory Routes and Areas are not marked on topographical navigation charts used for pilot navigation and to determine their existence and dimensions it will be necessary to refer to the RAC section of the UK Air Pilot.

Airmiss Reporting Procedures

On occasions during flight, aircraft may inadvertently come sufficiently close to one another so as to create a serious risk of airborne collision. In order to investigate and if possible to avoid repetition of such circumstances an Airmiss reporting procedure has been laid down.

Whenever a pilot considers that his aircraft may have been endangered by the proximity of another aircraft during flight within UK airspace to the extent that a definite risk of collision existed, such an incident should be reported as an *'Airmiss Report'*.

If radio is carried, the initial report of the incident can be made by RTF to the ATCU with which the aircraft is in communication at the time (prefixing the message with the word *AIRMISS*) or by telephone or other means to any UK ATSU immediately after landing.

Whichever method is used to make the initial report, it must be confirmed in writing by the pilot within 7 days of the incident. Form CA1094 should be used for this purpose and an example of the front side of this form is shown on the next page at Fig. 2-21.

The official investigation which takes place following such a report may indicate a *prima facie* offence under military or civil law and a pilot reporting an Airmiss may be required to make a formal statement to one of the police authorities. He may also be required to give evidence at military or civil legal proceedings.

When the investigation is complete, the pilot, and where appropriate the operating company of the aircraft concerned in the incident, will be advised officially of the findings and of any action that it has been possible to take to avoid a similar occurrence. When a Company is informed, a copy of the information will be sent to the pilot.

An Airmiss which takes place within the airspace of another State will not be investigated by the UK authorities. A pilot of a UK registered aircraft involved in such an incident should consult the Aeronautical Information Publication of that State and follow its National reporting procedure.

AIRMISS REPORT – PILOTS

Instructions for Use

1   **Pilots Reporting on Airmiss** This form should be used by Pilots to confirm and/or supplement details given in initial reports when such reports have been made by radio or telephone to an ATSU. This form should be used also by Pilots reporting on Airmiss if and when it has not been possible to make an initial report. When completed *this form must be sent direct* to Joint Airmiss Section, Hillingdon House, Uxbridge, Middlesex UB10 0RU (Uxbridge 31581 Ext. 644).

2   **Other Pilots** This form should be used by other Pilots involved in Airmisses to provide information as requested by the Joint Airmiss Section.

3   Detailed information on Airmiss Reporting Procedures is promulgated in the UK Air Pilot.

4   Shaded areas indicate items to be included in an initial report by radio.

	A	AIRMISS REPORT
1 Name of pilot in command 2 Flight deck crew complement	B	1 2
Operator	C	
Aircraft registration marks	D	
Aircraft type	E	
1 Radio call sign 2 In communication with 3 Frequency	F	1 2 3
Aerodrome of departure	G	
Aerodrome of first intended landing	H	
Type of flight plan	I	*IFR/VFR/None
1 Position of Airmiss 2 Aircraft heading 3 True airspeed	J	1 .... (Lat and Long) 2 .... *True/Magnetic 3 .... kn

1 Flight level, Altitude or Height
2 Altimeter setting
3 Aircraft attitude
4 Phase of flight
	K	1 *FL ..../................ ft
		2 .... mb (*standard/REG.QNH/QNH/QFE)
		3 *Level/Climbing/Descending/Turning (*Right/Left)
		4 *Take-off En route descent Circuit
		   Initial climb Holding Overshoot
		   En route climb Final descent Aerobatic
		   Cruise Landing Trg or Mil manoeuvres

Flight weather conditions at time of Airmiss	L	1 *IMC/VMC 2 Distance .... ft *Above/Below *Cloud/Fog/Haze 3 Distance .... Km/M horizontally from cloud 4 In *Rain/Snow/Sleet/Fog/Haze/Cloud/Between layers 5 Flying *into/out of sun 6 Flight visibility .... Km/M 7 *Day/Night/Twilight
Date and Time (GMT) of Airmiss	M	
Description of other aircraft if relevant: 1 Type, high/low wing, number of engines 2 Radio call sign, registration 3 Markings, colour, lighting 4 Other available details	N	1 2 3 4

CA 1094
011174

Please turn over

← **Airmiss Form**
Fig. 2-21

Civil Aviation Authority

Flight Plan Form
Fig. 2-22

| FLIGHT PLAN | ATS COPY |

(Flight plan form content)

Airspace Restrictions and Hazards

The airspace considered under this heading in as far as it is applicable to the UK, is basically divided into six types of area over which civil aircraft operations may for one reason or another be restricted, either temporarily, or permanently, on the grounds of safety. The six types of areas which represent a primary hazard to aircraft in flight are:

1. Danger Areas
2. Prohibited Areas
3. Restricted Areas
4. Military Flight Training Areas
5. Bird Sanctuaries
6. High Intensity Radio Transmission Areas

In addition there are several other areas or locations which present additional hazards or within which it is advisable to restrict aircraft movements.

7. In-Flight Refuelling Areas
8. Areas of Intense Air Activity
9. Glider Launching Sites
10. Certain Airspace (Outside Danger Areas) in which Pilotless Aircraft are manoeuvred
11. Target Towing Areas
12. Areas where Parachute Training Balloons are Flown
13. Locations where high obstructions are sited.

All of these areas and locations together with detailed information relating to them are promulgated in the RAC section of the UK Air Pilot. Additionally items 1 to 7 are also shown on the '*Chart of United Kingdom Airspace Restrictions*'. NOTAM and Aeronautical Information Circulars (AIC's) are also used to alert pilots to any changes which may occur in relation to their periods of activity.

Danger Areas:
These areas are captive balloon flying areas and weapon ranges, the latter including test and practice ranges for all types of weapons (guns, bombs, aircraft cannon and rocket etc.). It is emphasised that only the type of activity most likely to be encountered is listed. Pilots should, therefore, take every precaution to avoid infringing the boundaries of active danger areas regardless of the type of activity expected within the area. Pilots should also be aware that in the immediate vicinity of those Danger Areas in which military aircraft operate, many of those aircraft fly pre-set range patterns. Pilots of itinerant aircraft flying close to Danger Areas should therefore keep an especially sharp lookout for such aircraft and take any neccessary avoiding action as early as possible.

The UK Air Pilot only contains details of those danger areas within the UK Flight Information Regions which have an upper limit in excess of 500' above the local surface level (i.e. 500' above ground level or mean sea level as applicable). The attention of all pilots is drawn to the fact that there are many ranges, rifle, small arms etc, with upper limits of 500' agl/amsl or less. Pilots should therefore satisfy themselves that they are clear of such activity if forced to fly below 500'.

Danger Areas are of two types, Permanent (Scheduled) or Notified. Scheduled Areas are operational for laid down fixed periods which do not vary, for example these periods may be:

> 24 Hours of every day (H24)
>
> 24 Hours from Monday to Friday (H24 M–F)
>
> Day only
>
> Day only from Monday to Friday
>
> For specified hours and days

Note: In relation to Danger Areas '**Day**' means the period between 0800 to 1800 Local Time.

Scheduled Danger Areas are coded and shown on the '**Chart of UK Airspace Restrictions**' with a solid red outline to indicate their geographic dimensions.

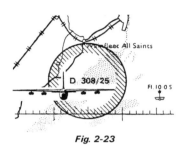

Fig. 2-23

Because the UK Danger Areas are situated within the latitudes 49N to 59N, a simple code designation has been arranged in that the first number e.g. *3* in the illustration on the left, shows the area is situated in the geographic region between 53N and 54N, if the first number had been *4* then this would indicate that it was situated in the region between 54N and 55N.

The letter and numbers D308 in Fig. 2-23 is the identification code of the particular Danger Area. The numbers 25 after the oblique stroke give the upper limit in thousands of feet above mean sea level, i.e. 25.000'.

Notified Danger Areas are those areas whose operational periods vary and information relating to their operational activity is given by NOTAM. The code figures of these areas have the same meanings as for Permanent (Scheduled) Danger Areas but the geographic boundaries are shown on the Chart of UK Airspace Restrictions by a broken red outline.

Although the same presentation of solid or broken red outlines are used on topographical maps and charts to depict Permanent or Notified Danger Areas it will be necessary to refer to the UK Air Pilot and NOTAMS to establish when Notified Danger Areas are active.

Prohibited and Restricted Areas
These areas normally related to the airspace within the immediate vicinity of Atomic Energy or Security Establishments. They are promulgated in the UK Air Pilot and on the Chart of UK Airspace Restrictions which also shows their vertical and geographic dimensions.

Prohibited Areas are indicated on maps and charts by the letter **P** and are permanent H24 throughout the year. Pilots must at all times avoid flying within these areas. Certain Atomic Energy or Security Establishments are situated in the close vicinity of the approach paths of airfields and in these circumstances a modification to the rules is made and the areas is designated a Restricted Area.

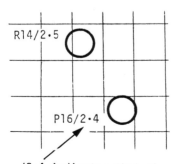

Within Restricted Areas, aircraft may only operate for the purposes of entry/exit to the particular airfields. Nevertheless a minimum height restriction may apply. Restricted Areas are depicted on maps and charts with the letter **R**.

/2·4 indicates that the vertical extent of the Area is from the surface to 2400' amsl.

Military Flight Training Areas

These are areas of Upper Airspace (above flight level 245) of defined dimensions within which intense military flying training takes place. Such areas are normally above the levels used by private pilots and reference to them in this manual is for general information only.

There are however many Low Level Routes along which military high speed flying takes place. The U.K. authorities publish information of the Military Low Level System, but this does not include all low level routes used by military aircraft. Pilots must therefore be especially vigilant when operating below 1000′ outside aerodrome traffic zones.

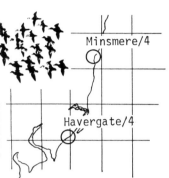

Bird Sanctuaries

These are particular areas in which large colonies of birds are known to breed. They normally extend from ground/sea level up to 4000′ and information relating to their geographic and vertical limits is shown on topographical maps and the Chart of UK Airspace Restrictions. The figure **4** shown in the adjacent illustration indicates a top limit of 4000′.

Pilots are specifically requested to avoid these areas, especially during any stated breeding season. Apart from the ecological nuisance of aircraft flying within these areas there also exists a very high risk of aircraft bird strikes with attendant hazards to aircraft in flight. Information on bird migration and areas of bird concentrations is given in the UK Air Pilot and when large concentrations of bird movements are known to be taking place '***Bird Warning Movement Messages***' are promulgated in NOTAMS.

High Intensity Radio Transmission Areas

There are a number of these areas within the UK. The installations based within them emit radio energy of an intensity which may cause interference to and sometimes damage to aircraft radio equipment as well as possible harmful bodily effects if the aircraft remains in the vicinity for an appreciable period.

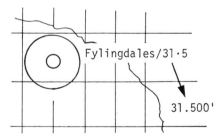

The vertical dimensions which such interference can reach vary from 1000′ to above 10,000′ amsl so they must be treated with respect and avoided whenever possible.

These areas are not shown on topographical charts and reference will need to be made to the UK Air Pilot or Chart of UK Airspace Restrictions during flight planning operations.

Additional Hazards to Aircraft in Flight

The areas which are listed as '*additional hazards to aircraft in flight*' are all clearly defined in the UK Air Pilot and (with the exception of No's 7, 10 and 11 on Page 2-39) also shown on topographical charts. Consideration will need to be given to these areas during pre-flight planning.

Glider sites may have winching cables extending up to 1500′ above the surface, and additionally tug aircarft carrying towing cables may be operating up to considerable altitudes. The sport of Free Fall Parachuting has also increased considerably over recent years and parachutists may be dropping from up to 10,000′ and above.

A final note is that temporary areas such as those used during Military Air Exercises, Flying Displays, Air Races etc., will be established for short periods throughout the year. The geographic and vertical dimensions of these areas together with their times of operation will be promulgated by NOTAM.

Navigation Obstructions
In the United Kingdom an '***Air Navigation Obstruction***' is defined as any building or work, including waste heaps, which attains or exceeds a height of 300' above ground level (agl). Details of those obstructions of which the CAA has been informed, are listed in the RAC Section of the Air Pilot. Additionally, obstructions within 4 nm of an aerodrome reference point are listed in the AGA Section.

Whenever obstructions are listed in the Air Pilot their exact positions are shown together with their heights above ground level and above sea level. In the case of tall masts, the position of the centre of the mast is given but it should be noted that the stays or guys may spread out for a considerable distance.

In cases where a number of buildings, works or masts form the obstruction, the approximate centre of the site is given.

Those air navigation obstructions which are 500' or more above ground level are lighted. Lighting is in the form of a red obstruction light or lights, positioned on or near the highest point of the obstruction. Additional lights may be positioned at different heights on the obstruction. Deatails of unserviceability and return to serviceability, when notified to the CAA, will be promulgated by Class I NOTAM.

Air navigation obstructions between 300' and 500' agl are sometimes lighted as noted above, but details of unserviceabilities of lights on these obstructions will not normally be promulgated.

Details of all air navigation obstructions known at the date of the chart's preparation are shown on the topographical maps published by the CAA. This information will indicate whether or not the obstruction is normally lighted.

Royal Flights

Flights by Her Majesty the Queen and certain other members of the Royal Family are classified as '***Royal Flights***'. When these flights are made in fixed wing aircraft and in order to reduce the risk of collision with other aircraft, Royal Flights are conducted where possible within existing controlled airspace. Where this is not possible, temporary controlled airspace in the form of a '***Purple Airway***' or '***Zone***' will be established to cover the Royal route.

Irrespective of the weather conditions, all controlled airspace used for this purpose, whether of a permanent or temporary nature, will be notified as being IFR. Details of Royal Flights will be promulgated by a Special RF NOTAM.

When a Royal Flight is made in a helicopter, no special ATC procedures are employed, but the route(s) being used (including times) will be promulgated by a RF Notam and pilots flying in the vicinity of these routes are requested to keep an especially alert lookout for the aircraft.

The Aerodromes (AGA) Section of the Air Pilot

Information relating to aerodromes in the UK is promulgated in the Air Pilot which is amended at regular intervals and additionally NOTAMS are used to promulgate changes of a temporary nature, or items which are considered too important to wait for the next issue of the Air Pilot amendment service.

The AGA section of the Air Pilot gives details of all major airports and licensed aerodromes. It also contains information of unlicensed and military aerodromes available for use by civil aircraft.

Information relating to private landing strips is not given in the Air Pilot but details of a large number of such landing areas as well as licensed and unlicensed aerodromes can be obtained from the '*Air Touring Flight Guide*' which is published by Airtour Associates International Ltd., Elstree Aerodrome, Herts., London. This guide is published annually and an amendment service provides for eight amendment bulletins each year.

Civil Aerodromes

AGA 1 of the Air Pilot lists all customs airports which can be used for entry to, or departure from the UK. The physical characteristics of these airports, e.g. runways, facilities, local flying restrictions etc. are covered in AGA 2.

Information on the physical characteristics and facilities of smaller aerodromes is contained in AGA 3 and at the rear of this section is a supplement which gives additional information relating to any Special Instructions, Restrictions, Warnings, Obstructions and Safety Altitudes.

Figure 2-24 is an example of how information relating to major airports is presented in AGA 2, and Fig. 2-25 shows the method of presenting information on smaller aerodromes in AGA 3. All information in the Air Pilot is updated at regular intervals and the heavy black arrows seen in the margins of Figs. 24 and 25 are used to call the attention of pilots to changes which have occurred in relation to the previous issue of Air Pilot pages.

Figure 2-26 is an illustration of how additional information relating to certain local procedures is promulgated and Fig. 2-27 shows how aerodrome obstructions and safety altitudes are presented for the specific aerodromes.

Aerodromes as distinct from private landing strips operate throughout certain time periods of the day or night and in order that the pilot can determine whether a particular aerodrome is open or closed during the period of his intended flight a '*Schedule of Hours*' section is promulgated in the Air Pilot at AGA 5. Figure 2-28 shows an example of how this information is presented.

Another important section of the Air Pilot is the COM Section which gives details of the RTF frequencies, radio navigation equipment and let down aids which are available at specific aerodromes.

A specimen page from the COM Section of the Air Pilot showing how such information is promulgated is illustrated at Fig. 2-29.

A further point in relation to the COM Section is that it contains the RTF frequencies used by ATC to control air traffic in specific Control Zones, Airways, Terminal Areas and those areas of Flight Information Regions which are outside controlled airspace.

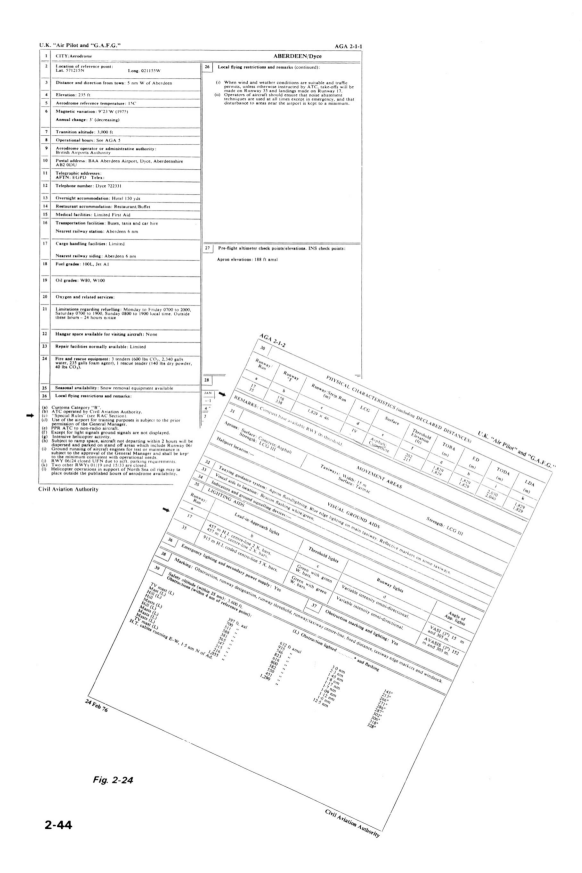

1	CITY/Aerodrome		ABERDEEN/Dyce

2	Location of reference point: Lat. 571215N Long. 021155W

3	Distance and direction from town: 5 nm W of Aberdeen

4	Elevation: 235 ft

5	Aerodrome reference temperature: 1°C

6	Magnetic variation: 9°23′ W (1975) Annual change: 3′ (decreasing)

7	Transition altitude: 3,000 ft

8	Operational hours: See AGA 5

9	Aerodrome operator or administrative authority: British Airports Authority

10	Postal address: BAA Aberdeen Airport, Dyce, Aberdeenshire AB2 0DU

11	Telegraphic addresses: AFTN: EGPD Telex:

12	Telephone number: Dyce 722331

13	Overnight accommodation: Hotel 150 yds

14	Restaurant accommodation: Restaurant/Buffet

15	Medical facilities: Limited First Aid

16	Transportation facilities: Buses, taxis and car hire Nearest railway station: Aberdeen 6 nm

17	Cargo handling facilities: Limited Nearest railway siding: Aberdeen 6 nm

18	Fuel grades: 100L, Jet A1

19	Oil grades: W80, W100

20	Oxygen and related services:

21	Limitations regarding refuelling: Monday to Friday 0700 to 2000, Saturday 0700 to 1900, Sunday 0800 to 1900 local time. Outside these hours – 24 hours notice

22	Hangar space available for visiting aircraft: None

23	Repair facilities normally available: Limited

24	Fire and rescue equipment: 3 tenders (600 lbs CO_2, 2,340 galls water, 235 galls foam agent), 1 rescue tender (140 lbs dry powder, 40 lbs CO_2).

25	Seasonal availability: Snow removal equipment available

26	Local flying restrictions and remarks:

(a) Customs Category "B".
(b) ATC operated by Civil Aviation Authority.
(c) "Special Rules" (see RAC Section).
(d) Use of the airport for training purposes is subject to the prior permission of the General Manager.
(e) PPR ATC to non-radio aircraft.
(f) Except for light signals ground signals are not displayed.
(g) Intensive helicopter activity.
(h) Subject to ramp space, aircraft not departing within 2 hours will be dispersed and parked on stand off areas which include Runway 06/
(i) Ground running of aircraft engines for test or maintenance is subject to the approval of the General Manager and shall be kept to the minimum consistent with operational needs.
(j) RWY 06/24 closed UFN due to acft. parking requirements.
(k) Two other RWYs 01/19 and 15/33 are closed.
(l) Helicopter operations in support of North Sea oil rigs may ta place outside the published hours of aerodrome availability.

Civil Aviation Authority

26	Local flying restrictions and remarks (continued):

(i) When wind and weather conditions are suitable and traffic permits, unless otherwise instructed by ATC, take-offs will be made on Runway 35 and landings made on Runway 17.
(ii) Operators of aircraft should ensure that noise abatement techniques are used at all times except in emergency, and that disturbance to areas near the airport is kept to a minimum.

27	Pre-flight altimeter check points/elevations. INS check points: Apron elevations: 188 ft amsl

28	
	JAN
	– 1
	4
	7

30	Runway/Run	Runway 'T'	PHYSICAL CHARACTERISTICS (including DECLARED DISTANCES)								
	a	b	Runway/Strip Run (m)	LCG	Surface	Threshold Elevation (ft)	TORA (m)	ED (m)	TODA (m)	LDA (m)
	17 35	156 338	c 1,829 × 46	d IV	e Asphalt Composite	f 203 215	g 1,829 1,829	h 1,829 1,829	i 2,010 2,040	k 1,829 1,829

31	REMARKS: Compass base available RWY 06 threshold.

	Aprons: Surface: Concrete Asphalt Strength: LCG III

	Heliport location —

32	MOVEMENT AREAS
	Taxiways: Width: 15 m Surface: Tarmac Strength: LCG III

33	Taxying guidance system: Apron floodlighting. Blue edge lighting on main taxiway. Reflective markers on some taxiways.

34	Visual aids to location: Beacon flashing white green.

35	Indicators and ground signalling devices —

35	LIGHTING AIDS		VISUAL GROUND AIDS

	Runway/Run	Lead-in/Approach lights	Threshold lights	Runway lights	Angle of App lights
	a	b	c	d	e
35		457 m H.I. centre-line 2 X. bars. 457 m L.I. centre-line 2 X. bars. 915 m H.I. coded centre-line 5 X. bars.	Green W. bars	Variable intensity omni-directional.	VASI (3°) 15 m and 305 m
			Green with green W. bars		AVASIS (3°) 152 m and 305 m

36	Emergency lighting and secondary power supply:

37	Obstruction marking and lighting: Yes

38	Marking: Obstruction, runway designation, runway threshold, runway/taxiway centre-line, fixed distance, taxiway edge markers and windsock.

39	Safety altitude (within 25 nm): 3,600 ft. Obstructions (within 4 nm of reference point):

	Obstructions		(L) Obstruction lighted .... • and flashing

	TV mast (L)	397 ft. aal	632 ft amsl
	Mast (L)	700 ″	915 ″
	Hill (L)	131 ″	746 ″
	Hill (L)	389 ″	823 ″
	Masts (L)	581 ″	818 ″
	Hill (L)	565 ″	800 ″
	Mast (L)	592 ″	592 ″
	Masts (L)	347 ″	550 ″
	Masts (L)	451 ″	451 ″
	H.T. mast (L)	216 ″	1,290 ″
	H.T. cables running E–W. 1.5 nm N of Ad	1,035 ″	

	3.0 nm	145°
	2.2 nm	213°
	4.5 nm	275°
	1.8 nm	286°
	1.7 nm	302°
	1.7 nm	306°
	0.9 nm	318°
	1.2 nm	328°
	1.0 nm	
	1.2 nm	
	12.5 nm	

24 Feb 76

Civil Aviation Authority

Fig. 2-24

AERODROME DIRECTORY—LAND

TOWN/ AERODROME CO-ORDINATES AND LOCATION	ELEV (ft.)	VAR	RUNWAY						DECLARED DISTANCES				SURFACE ELEVATIONS (ft.)				LIGHTING					GROUND SERVICES	OPERATOR ('PHONE NO.) AND REMARKS
			MAG	TRUE	DIMENSIONS (METRES)	S	STRENGTH	THRES ELEV (ft.)	TORA (m.)	ED (m.)	TODA (m.)	LDA (m.)	START OF TORA	END OF TORA	END OF ED	END OF TODA	A	L	T	R	OTHER		
1	2	3	4	5	6	7	8	9	10	11	12	13	14	15	16	17	18	19	20	21	22	23	24
ABERDEEN/Dyce	*See* AGA 2-1.																						
Abingdon 514125N 011845W 5 nm SSW of Oxford.	260	8°W	08 26		1,463 × 46		A		1,450 1,450	1,450 1,450	1,680 1,590	1,450 1,450							X	X	Ibn. Obs. Tax VASIS (18/36)		RAF (Abingdon 288). PPR to charter and private acft. †First 152 m. of Runway 18 sterile. Balloon flying. Runway 18—right hand circuits. Free fall parachuting from up to FL 120. See page AGA 3–35.
			18 36		2,012 × 46†		A	LCG V	2,010 2,010	2,010 2,010	2,150 2,010	1,855 2,010				X			X	X			
Alderney	*See* AGA 2-2.																						
AUCHTER-ARDER/Strathallan 561930N 034450W 4 nm SE of Crieff (Unlicensed)	120	10°W	10 28	089 269	1,006 × 31		G																Cirrus Aviation Ltd. (Auchterarder 2545 and Muthill 265). PPR. Parachuting takes place during daylight hours.
AYLESBURY/Thame 514632N 005620W 5 nm WSW of Aylesbury. (Unlicensed)	289	8°W	N/S		853 × 107		G															F—80 R.H.	Airtech. Ltd. (Haddenham, Bucks. 291422). PPR. Glider launching weekends.
			ENE/ WSW		1,082 × 107		G																
Banff 5740N 0238W 6 nm W of Banff	280	9°	11 29	100 280	688 × 20		C	265 280	688 688	688 688	688 688	688 688											Banff Flying Club—Sec.: Mr. W. I. Flett (Banff 2342). PPR. No facilities or ground services.
Barra 570125N 072625W Foreshore of Traigh Mhor.	Sea level	12°W	07 25	061 241	853 × 46		S		853 853	853 853	853 853	853 853											Loganair Ltd. (Northbay 283). PPR from 041-889-3181. Ad. is below high water mark. Boards mark the strips.
			11 29	101 281	732 × 46		S		732 732	732 732	732 732	732 732											
			15 33	141 321	914 × 46		S		914 914	945 914	945 914	914 914											

Fig. 2-25

AERODROME DIRECTORY

Special Instructions, Restrictions, Warnings, etc.

Additional to any given in the Aerodrome Directory column 24.

Abingdon   Warning

1. Caution is necessary on approach to Runway 26. Houses and television aerials form an obstruction, height 30 feet agl, 457 metres from touchdown.

2. Aircraft inbound to Abingdon are to call Benson Approach or Abingdon at least 5 nm before the boundary of Benson/Abingdon MATZ or be under control of Heathrow Radar.

BELFAST/ Harbour   Local Flying Regulations

1. Right-hand circuit when Runway 05 is in use.

2. Many obstacles on approach to Runway 05. See AGA 3-39.

Brough   Warning

1. A chimney (lighted) 1.3 nm bearing 101°T has been constructed with a height of 612 feet aal, 625 feet amsl. Pilots are warned to exercise caution when using this aerodrome.

Church Fenton   Warning

1. A public road crosses approach to Runways 06 and 34.

Culdrose   Warnings and Local Flying Regulations

1. Extreme caution is necessary at this aerodrome and at the satellite of Predannack (50°00'N 05°13'W) due to extensive helicopter flying.

2. No aircraft can be allowed in the Culdrose circuit unless it is in RTF communication with the Control Tower. Fixed-wing aircraft joining are to contact Approach Control at 20 nm.

3. No visual signals permissible.

4. GCA letdown mandatory for fixed-wing aircraft.

Cumbernauld   Local Flying Regulation

1. In IFR, suitably equipped aircraft may let down at Edinburgh and proceed to Cumbernauld VMC.

Doncaster   Warning

1. Pilots are warned to avoid the aerodrome traffic zones of RAF Finningley and Lindholme.

Fig. 2-26

AERODROME DIRECTORY (contd.)
Aerodrome Obstructions and Safety Altitudes

Aerodrome Obstructions. Details are given of obstructions within 4 nautical miles of the centre of the aerodrome-exceptionally beyond 4 nautical miles. The datum point from which the distances and bearings are quoted is the Aerodrome Reference Point (ARP) or, where no official ARP is established, the approximate centre of the landing area. The co-ordinates of the ARP or datum point are given in column 1 of the Schedule of Aerodromes. The heights of obstructions above aerodrome level are all related to the aerodrome elevation. All bearings are in degrees True.

Safety Altitude. The Safety Altitude quoted provides safe vertical clearance of 1,000 ft. above the highest known obstacle within 25 nautical miles of the relevant aerodrome.

Safety Altitudes and Obstructions at Airports listed in AGA 2. Details are not included in this tabulation but are given for the individual airport in AGA 2.

Abbreviations

aal — Above aerodrome level		L — Lighted
agl — Above ground level		nm — Nautical miles
amsl — Above mean sea level		SA — Safety Altitude
Ad — Aerodrome		

ABERDEEN/Dyce—Safety Altitude 3,600 ft.

TV mast (L)	397 ft. aal	632 ft. amsl	3·0	nm	145°
Mast (L)	700 ,,	935 ,,	2·3	nm	213°
Hill (L)	511 ,,	746 ,,	1·45	nm	266°
Hill	588 ,,	823 ,,	1·8	nm	271°
Masts (L)	381 ,,	616 ,,	1·17	nm	286°
Hill (L)	565 ,,	800 ,,	1·7	nm	287°
Masts (L)	347 ,,	582 ,,	1·09	nm	302°
Masts (L)	315 ,,	550 ,,	1·12	nm	306°
Masts (L)	216 ,,	451 ,,	1·0	nm	318°
TV Mast (L)	1,055 ,,	1,290 ,,	12·5	nm	328°

H.T. cables running E–W, 1·5 nm N of Ad.

Abingdon—Safety Altitude 2,200 ft.

AUCHTERARDER/Strathallan—Safety Altitude 5,000 ft.
Trees to W and SW of airfield.

AYLESBURY/Thame—Safety Altitude 2,200 ft.
Aerial, 75 ft. aal, 364 ft. amsl at the W boundary of aerodrome.

Banff—Safety Altitude 3,800 ft.

Barra—Safety Altitude 3,500 ft.
High ground rising to 338 ft. amsl within 0·9 nm to N.
High ground rising to 294 ft. amsl within 2·3 nm to NE.
High ground rising to 680 ft. amsl within 1·4 nm to S.
High ground rising to 1,260 ft. amsl within 3·5 nm to SW.
Telegraph wires 20 ft. amsl, adjacent to W boundary of landing area.

BARROW/Walney Island—Safety Altitude 4,300 ft.

High ground	203 ft. aal	250 ft. amsl	1·97 nm	055°
High ground	228 ,,	275 ,,	1·59 nm	068°
H.T. pylon	189 ,,	236 ,,	0·99 nm	096°
H.T. pylon	162 ,,	209 ,,	1·20 nm	105°
Cooling tower	173 ,,	220 ,,	1·66 nm	118°
Chimney	88 ,,	135 ,,	1·65 nm	120°
Chimney	178 ,,	225 ,,	0·87 nm	125°
Chimney	238 ,,	285 ,,	0·87 nm	129°
Mast	189 ,,	236 ,,	1·58 nm	130°

BARROW/Walney Island (cont.)

Chimney	168 ft. aal	215 ft. amsl	0·89 nm	132°
Crane	217 ,,	264 ,,	1·47 nm	159°

Slag bank up at 100 ft. aal extends N–S for ½ mile at 0·7 nm E of Ad.

BATH RACECOURSE/Lansdowne—Safety Altitude 3,000 ft.

BEDFORD/Castle Mill—Safety Altitude 2,000 ft.

Chimney	325 ft. aal	407 ft. amsl	0·7 nm	244°

H.T. cables running ESE–WNW 0·49 nm to NE.

BELFAST/Harbour—Safety Altitude 3,300 ft.

3 chimneys (L)	170 ft. aal	185 ft. amsl	0·8 nm	006°
Spire	185 ,,	200 ,,	2·0 nm	043°
Spire (L)	219 ,,	234 ,,	0·7 nm	175°
Chimney (L)	183 ,,	198 ,,	1·17 nm	202°
Chimney (L)	166 ,,	181 ,,	1·15 nm	214°
Gasholder	246 ,,	261 ,,	2·2 nm	226°
Cranes (L)	315 ,,	330 ,,	0·66 nm	240°
Chimney	246 ,,	261 ,,	2·9 nm	242°
Spire	206 ,,	221 ,,	2·5 nm	248°
TV mast (L)*	1,713 ,,	1,728 ,,	5·1 nm	253°
TV mast (L)	1,684 ,,	1,699 ,,	4·7 nm	261°
Grain silo	186 ,,	201 ,,	1·3 nm	261°
Chimney	206 ,,	221 ,,	1·6 nm	271°
Mast (L)	1,336 ,,	1,351 ,,	4·12 nm	292°

H.T. Pylons 120 ft. aal 0·49 nm from threshold of Runway 05.
High ground rising to 644 ft. amsl within 2·4 nm to E and S.
High ground rising to 1,237 ft. amsl to W and NW.
Floating cranes and shipping in Belfast Harbour.
Three cranes (L), 150 ft. aal on W side.
Two chimneys (L), height 250 ft. aal, 1 nm W of Ad.
Four chimneys (L) parallel with runway, 800 m. N and W of 23 threshold, 170 ft. aal, 185 ft. amsl.
Travelling crane (L) hazard beacon, 364ft. amsl 1·22 nm 235°.
Crane (L) 81 ft. aal, 96 ft. amsl, 1,448 m. from 23 threshold on extended runway centre-line.

*Flashes 30 times a minute.

Fig. 2-27

→ **SCHEDULE OF HOURS**

Civil Aviation Authority

1. All times are in GMT and are daily—including Sundays—unless otherwise stated. Where "SS" or "SS+ .." is shown as an alternative closing time, the aerodrome or service closes at whichever time is earlier, unless otherwise stated.

2. The two categories of Air Traffic Control Unit which are referred to in columns 4 and 8 below have the following significance:—

   L—Licensed—The persons providing the service are required by the Rules of the Air and Air Traffic Control Regulations 1974, or by the appropriate authority, to hold ATC licences including appropriate ratings valid at that place. The competence of the persons providing the service is subject to inspection by the Civil Aviation Authority.

   U—Unlicensed—The persons providing the service are not required to hold valid ATC licences and the service is not subject to inspection by the Civil Aviation Authority.

   Where no category is indicated the aerodrome is either:—

   (a) A Service aerodrome, in which case the categories do not apply: or
   (b) A Civil aerodrome where no ATC service is provided.

3. Military aerodromes which can be used on prior permission are not shown in this schedule. Application for use should be made direct to the aerodrome concerned.

4. **Abbreviations used in Schedule**

H24	Continuous service	SS	Sunset
HJ	Sunrise to sunset	SS+	Sunset plus . . . . minutes
HJ+	Sunrise to . . . . minutes after sunset	Wkd.	Weekdays (Mon.—Sat.)

AERODROME OR ZONE 1	AERODROME AVAILABLE FOR USE 2	AIR TRAFFIC CONTROL UNIT HOURS 3	CAT. 4	AERODROME OR ZONE 5	AERODROME AVAILABLE FOR USE 6	AIR TRAFFIC CONTROL UNIT HOURS 7	CAT. 8
ABERDEEN/Dyce ..	★0600–2050	As for aerodrome	L	BELFAST/Aldergrove ..	★H24	As for aerodrome	L
Alderney ..	0700–1830 (and by arrangement)	0630–1830 (and by arrangement)	L	BELFAST/Harbour ..	★0800–1530 Mon.–Fri. (and by arrangement)	As for aerodrome	L
				Bembridge	0800–1900 or SS	—	
AUCHTERARDER/ Strathallan	★By arrangement	—		Benbecula	★By arrangement (3 hours notice) 0815–1530 Mon., Thu. 0845–1530 Tue., Wed., Fri. 0900–1400 Sat. (and by arrangement)	As for aerodrome	L
AYLESBURY/Thame ..	★By arrangement	—					
Banff ..	★By arrangement	—					
Barra	★By arrangement (tide permitting)	—		Biggin Hill	★0800–2000 or SS Sat., Sun. and Public Holidays. 0800–2000 Mon.–Fri. (and by arrangement)	As for aerodrome	U
BARROW/Walney Island ..	★0700–1600 Mon.–Fri. (and by arrangement)	As for aerodrome	U				
BATH RACECOURSE/ Lansdowne	★Race-days only	—		BIGGLESWADE/ Old Warden	★By arrangement	—	
BEDFORD/Castle Mill ..	★On request SR–SS	—					
Belfast Control Zone ..	—	H24	L*	Birmingham Control Zone ..		H24	L

★ AERODROME IS AVAILABLE SUBJECT TO CONDITIONS OF USE—SEE APPROPRIATE SCHEDULE.

RADIO COMMUNICATION AND NAVIGATION FACILITIES

STATION	SERVICE	CALL SIGN OR IDENTIFICATION	EM	TRANSMITS kHz	TRANSMITS MHz	RECEIVES kHz	RECEIVES MHz	HOURS OF SERVICE (GMT)	CO-ORDINATES	TO AERODROME MAG	TO AERODROME NM	OPERATING AUTHORITY AND REMARKS
1	2	3	4	5	6	7	8	9	10	11	12	13
Aberdeen	VOR	ADN	A9	—	114·3	—	—	H24 except 1230–1430 4th Tue. of each month.	571839N 021557W	—	—	VOR/DME co-located and freq. paired. Protection Range/Altitude 100 nm/50,000 ft. (200 nm/50,000 ft. in sector 059°–169° M)
	DME	ADN	P	—	1177	—	1114	H24 except 1230–1630 1st Tue. of each month.	571839N 021557W	—	—	DME Ch. 90X.
ABERDEEN/Dyce	ATC	Aberdeen Approach	A3	—	†126·1	—	†126·1	0600–2050	—	—	—	†126·1 MHz for North Sea hel. ops only.
	APP	Aberdeen Approach	A3	—	120·4	—	120·4		—	—	—	ø120·4 MHz VDF can be changed to 118·1 MHz O/R.
	VDF	Aberdeen Homer	A3	—	ø120·4 / 121·25	—	ø120·4 / 121·25		571407N 021255W	173	2·0	
	TWR	Aberdeen Tower	A3	—	118·1	—	118·1		—	—	—	
	ILS	I-AX (The localiser usable coverage sector is ± 35° about the nominal course line. See also COM 0-2)	A2	—	109·9 333·8	—	—	As for ATC. ATC will advise when ILS not available because of maintenance, normally Sundays for up to 4 hrs.	—	167	—	ICAO Facility Performance Category I. Glide path 3°, Localiser 300·3 m from THR 35, MM 1372 m, OM 3·82 nm from THR 17. ILS Ref Datum Hgt 51 ft.
	NDB	ADN (Not to be used for holding, let-down or approach aid unless the ATC services are available)	A0A2	377	—	—	—	H24	571608N 021453W	167	3·82	Range 50 nm. Located at ILS OM.
Alderney	VOR	ALD (Not to be used as holding, let-down or approach aid unless Alderney airport ATC services are available. The cone of the VOR is not to be used for psn. reporting when approaching from south)	A9	—	112·2	—	—	H24 except 1230–1430 2nd Wed. of each month.	494222N 021305W	—	—	VOR/DME co-located and freq. paired. Protection Range/Altitude 60 nm/25,000 ft. DME Ch. 59X.
	DME	ALD	P	—	1020	—	1083	H24 except 0830–1230 2nd Thu. of each month.				

Fig. 2-29

Note: The information from the illustrations on pages 2-44 to 2-47 is not necessarily current and therefore it must not be used for flight planning purposes.

Military Aerodromes

Certain military aerodromes are notified as being available to civil aircraft and these aerodromes are listed in AGA2, together with details of their physical characteristics and facilities in the same manner as for civil aerodromes.

Details of the RTF frequencies available at these airfields are also included in the COM Section of the Air Pilot. Nevertheless it should be remembered that except for those circumstances necessitating in-flight diversion or emergency situations, permission to use any military airfield must be obtained before commencing a flight.

Aerodrome Ground Lights

These are installed at various civil and military aerodromes within the United Kingdom and are of the following two main types:

Identification Beacons

These exhibit a two letter morse group at a speed equivalent to 6 to 8 words a minute every 12 seconds. When installed at civil aerodromes, their colour is green and when installed at military aerodromes their colour is red.

Aerodrome Beacons

These are not normally provided at aerodromes where an Identification Beacon is installed. Aerodrome Beacons emit a flashing white/green light but a few aerodromes in the UK have Beacons which only flash white.

2-47

Time of Operation
Any of these beacons may be operated in daylight hours during conditions of poor visibility, and at other times during the ATC hours of watch, e.g. during any period when night flying operations are being conducted at the particular aerodrome.

Royal Air Force and Royal Navy Master Aerodromes
Certain RAF and RN aerodromes are designated '**Master Aerodromes**'. These are operational throughout 24 hours each day, and at these aerodromes identification beacons will operate continuously throughout the hours of darkness.

Other Royal Air Force and Royal Navy Aerodromes
At these aerodromes the operation of Identification Beacons will depend upon military flying commitments and as such they may be switched on at any time during the day or night.

Meteorology

The need to obtain current weather information is vital to the safe operation of an aircraft. In order to meet this need an aviation section has been established within the National Meteorological Centre based at Bracknell in Berkshire.

Sources of Information
The activities of the various departments of this complex and highly sophisticated technical establishment rely upon an enormous network of information services which relay world wide weather information from observation stations to its aviation section.

The information from some 2.200 weather reports made every 3 hours is collated, analysed and interpreted. From these weather reports, forecasts of the UK weather situation are made and passed to various meteorological units based at aerodromes throughout the country.

All licensed aerodromes receive area forecasts daily covering each six hour period. This forecast is issued for a specific area covering a certain radius from the aerodrome concerned.

Requests for Route Forecasts
When long routes are planned, a Route Forecast should be obtained from the appropriate meteorological unit, and this is normally issued in the form of a Significant Weather Chart covering the whole of the route length. At least 2 hours notice will be required by the meteorological unit prior to the issue of a Route Forecast and when the route length is over 500nm, 4 hours notice will be required.

An '**Actual Weather Report**' for the destination aerodrome can only be obtained by contacting the ATC unit at the aerodrome concerned. This unit may also have some information relating to the weather trend at the aerodrome for a short period ahead.

The appropriate meteorological stations to contact for Route Forecasts are listed together with their telephone numbers and hours of operation in the UK Air Pilot Section MET 2. Requests for meteorological forecasts should contain the following information:
> Details of intended route.
> The height to be flown.
> The time period (GMT) of the planned flight.
> The time at which the forecast is to be collected.

Note: Detailed information relating to Area and Route Forecasts is given in the Aviation Meteorology Section contained in Manual 2.

Facilitation

Arrival, Departure and Transit of Civil Aircraft on International Flights
When an aircraft leaves or enters the National Boundaries of the United Kingdom, the pilot must arrange Customs Clearance at a notified Customs Airport.

It must however be appreciated that some Customs Airports are not available throughout 24 hours each day and it is the responsibility of the pilot who is entering or leaving the UK to ensure that he lands at an airport at which Customs facilities are available.

The aerodromes in the United Kingdom which have been designated as Customs and Excise Airports by the Department of Trade with the concurrence of the Commissioners of Customs and Excise are shown in the following list:—

ABERDEEN/Dyce	Leeds and Bradford
BELFAST/Aldergrove	Liverpool
Biggin Hill	LONDON/Gatwick
Birmingham	LONDON/Heathrow
Blackpool	LONDON/Stansted
BOURNEMOUTH/Hurn	Luton
BRISTOL/Lulsgate	Lydd
Cambridge	Manchester International
Cardiff	Manston
Coventry	Newcastle
East Midlands	Norwich
Edinburgh	PLYMOUTH/Roborough
Exeter	Prestwick
Glasgow	Southampton
GLOUCESTER AND CHELTENHAM/	Southend
Staverton	Sumburgh
Humberside	Tees-side
ISLE OF MAN/Ronaldsway	Valley
Kirkwall	

Customs and excise attendance at these airports is provided according to the needs of regular air traffic and details of 'hours of availability' for each airport are given in the Air Pilot (FAL Section).

Private Flights, Documentary Requirements
Flights abroad which are of a private and temporary nature will need to meet the following simple documentary procedure:
> The pilot will have to present to the Customs Officer, either a Carnet de Passages en Douane, or a Customs Form No. XS 29A in duplicate. The Carnet or duplicate copy of the completed Form XS 29A will be retained by the pilot, and presented to the Customs Officer on the aircraft's return to the UK.

It must be appreciated that aircraft are liable to Customs duty and all aircraft arriving in the UK from abroad are *prima facie* liable to Customs duty but this will not apply provided the above procedure has been carried out.

Customs Requirements

Aircraft flying to or from places abroad may cross the UK coastline at any point subject to the requirements of any regulations in force. All persons leaving or entering the UK must produce their baggage and articles carried with them for examination by the Customs Officer.

Flights to the Channel Islands and the Isle of Man are considered as flights abroad. When visiting the Isle of Man the first point of landing must be at Ronaldsway Airport, however, inbound flights from the Isle of Man to the UK need not land at a Customs Airport if the goods being carried have the same 'duty equivalent' as UK values.

After an aircraft has been cleared outbound from a UK Customs Airport, it must not land in the UK again other than at a Customs Airport. If for any reason a pilot has to force land after receiving Customs clearance outbound, or before receiving Customs clearance inbound, he must report the occurrence as quickly as possible either to the Customs authorities or to the local police.

He must also produce upon demand the documents relating to the flight and ensure that his passengers and any goods unloaded are kept in close vicinity to the aircraft unless it is necessary to move them for reasons of health, safety or preservation of life or property.

Public Health Requirements

The Health Laws of the United Kingdom permit an Airport Medical Officer to examine any crew member or passenger entering the UK:—

> *'Who is suspected of suffering from, or been exposed to an infectious disease or is suspected of being verminous'*

He may also examine any person intending to depart from the UK if there are reasonable grounds for believing that person is suffering from a (quarantinable) disease within the International Health Regulations.

A Medical Officer may require the crew or passengers to produce a valid international certificate of vaccination against 'Smallpox' if they have entered the UK from certain countries or areas. If a valid certificate of vaccination cannot be produced the person concerned may be offered vaccination and may be placed under health surveillance or in isolation for an appropriate period.

Search and Rescue

Search and Rescue is a life saving service provided for the safety of aircraft passengers and crew. The United Kingdom and surrounding waters within the FIR's and the Shanwick Oceanic Area (OCA) are divided into two regions for this purpose.

Responsibility and Organisation

The responsibility for co-ordinating search and rescue action lies with a joint Civil/Military Organisation which has a Rescue Co-ordination Centre in each region.

When the location of a civil aircraft which has crashed on land is known and no air search is necessary, responsibility for dealing with the incident devolves upon the civil ground organisation. A CAA Air Traffic Control Centre (ATCC), upon becoming aware of an aircraft in distress and knowing the position of its emergency landing, will notify the local police in the area who will then alert fire, ambulance and hospital services as appropriate.

At some places, arrangements are made for the fire service to be notified directly in order to save time in bringing this service into operation. Should the first report of an accident be given by a member of the public to the police, that force will immediately alert the fire and other services including the ATCC who will be informed of the rescue action being taken and given all relevant details.

The Rescue Co-ordination Centres can call upon a large number of resources whenever a 'Search and Rescue' operation is implemented, some examples of these are:

The Royal Air Force;
    Fixed Wing and Helicopter Aircraft
    Mountain Rescue Units
Royal National Lifeboat Institution
Ocean Station Vessels
Royal Navy Helicopters and Ships
HM Coastguard Service

The Aeronautical Emergency Service on RTF frequency 121.5 MHz should be used for distress communications. Distress and Diversion (D & D) ATC units of the Royal Air Force maintain a continuous listening watch on this frequency.

In the event of an aircraft having to force land in the sea, or sparsely populated or mountainous areas, the difficulties of the SAR operation will be increased and it is therefore a responsibility of all General Aviation pilots to ensure that when flights are planned over such areas, they carry appropriate survival equipment and file a flight plan, particularly if the aircraft is not equipped with radio.

Aircraft Not Equipped With Radio

A pilot of an aircraft not equipped with radio is strongly advised to file a flight plan if he intends to fly more than 10 nm from the coast or over sparsely populated or mountainous areas as this will assist rescue action should the aircraft be reported overdue.

Pilots should particularly note that flight plans can only be delivered to destinations which are on or linked to the Aeronautical Fixed Telecommunication Network (AFTN) and that prompt search action can only be initiated if an aircraft is reported overdue by the destination aerodrome.

Pilots intending to fly to destinations which are not connected to the AFTN should advise a responsible person at the destination of the intended flight and arrange for that person to notify the ATS authorities in the event of non-arrival.

The following areas within the UK are considered to be difficult from a Search and Rescue aspect:

Scotland
Hebrides, Orkneys and Shetlands
Pennine Range
Lake District
Yorkshire Moors
Welsh Mountains
Peak District of Derbyshire
Exmoor
Dartmoor

Non radio aircraft operating between the mainland and the Scilly Isles should follow the procedure outlined in the SAR Section of the UK Air Pilot.

Visual Distress and Urgency Signals
The visual Distress, Urgency and Safety Signals which are internationally established for use by aircraft are shown on pages 2-55 and 2-56. In addition to these signals a set of International Ground/Air Visual Signals are laid down for the use of survivors and search parties. These signals are shown in Fig. 2-30 below.

GROUND–AIR VISUAL CODE FOR USE BY SURVIVORS		
1	REQUIRE ASSISTANCE	V
2	REQUIRE MEDICAL ASSISTANCE	X
3	NO OR NEGATIVE	N
4	YES OR AFFIRMATIVE	Y
5	AM PROCEEDING IN THIS DIRECTION	↑
IF IN DOUBT USE INTERNATIONAL SYMBOL FOR DISTRESS		SOS

Fig. 2-30

In the event that such signals have to be made, the procedures outlined in the next few paragraphs should be followed where applicable.

Lay out these symbols by using strips of fabric, pieces of wood, stones or any other available material. Endeavour to provide as big a colour contrast as possible between the material used for the symbols and the background against which the symbols are exposed.

Symbols should be at least 2 to 3 metres in height and larger if possible. Care should be taken to lay out the symbols exactly as depicted in order to avoid confusion.

In addition to using these symbols, every effort should be made to attract attention by means of radio, flares, smoke, or any other available means.

If the ground is covered with snow, signals can be made by dragging, shovelling or trampling the snow. The symbols thus formed will appear to be black when seen from the air.

Survivors should also use any of the following methods to attract attention when aircraft, surface craft or search parties are heard or seen:

Make the aircraft as conspicuous as possible by spreading material (if available) over the wings and fuselage.

Use smoke or fire. A continuously burning fire is recommended with material ready to hand to cause it to smoke at short notice. A quantity of green branches or leaves, or oil, or rubber from the aircraft should produce the desired result. Three fires in the form of a triangle make a very good signal particularly at night.

Fire distress flares or cartridges.

Use some object with a bright flat surface as a heliograph.

Fly anything in the form of a flag and, if possible, make the international distress signal by flying a ball, or something resembling a ball, above or below it.

At night, flash torches or lights.

Procedures and Signals Employed by Rescue Aircraft
During the day, the pilot of the search aircraft will rock his wings to indicate that the survivors have been spotted. Certain rescue aircraft carry survival equipment which can be dropped by parachute.

The following technique is used when RAF aircraft are searching for survivors at night:

The search aircraft will fire a single green pyrotechnic at intervals of 5 to 10 minutes.

Survivors should then allow 15 seconds after they see the signal (so that the search aircraft can pass out of the glare). If the survivors have pyrotechnics available they should then fire a red pyrotechnic, followed after a short interval, by a second.

The survivors should fire additional pyrotechnics if the search aircraft appears to be getting off track, and when it is overhead, so that an accurate position can be obtained.

All pilots must have an understanding of the procedures to be followed during flight emergencies. Although there is no legislation applicable to the carriage of emergency equipment for private flights, a pilot's pre-flight planning should reflect his awareness of the possibility of emergency situations developing in unexpected circumstances, e.g.

Overwater flights not only demand the carriage of lifejackets but also require a passenger briefing on their operation and additionally, practice in wearing them whilst inside the aircraft.

When flight over sparsely populated territory is planned, it would be wise to carry some warm clothing and if possible to have some flares or smoke candles available and stowed in a secure position away from the cabin area where smoking may take place.

Only by paying attention to the possible consequences of a forced landing or ditching will the pilot meet the requirements of a good aircraft captain, and give his crew or passengers the best chance of survival.

SEARCH AND RESCUE REGIONS AND FACILITIES
(IN UNITED KINGDOM AND SURROUNDING WATERS AND IN SHANWICK OCA)

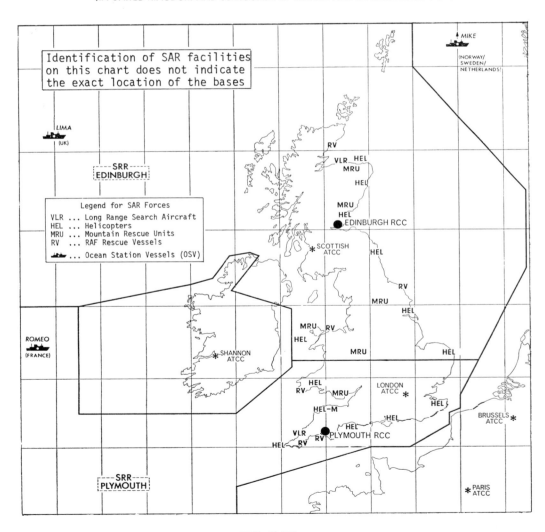

FIG. 2·31

Distress, Urgency and Safety Signals

Distress	
The following signals given, either together or separately, before the sending of a message, signify that an aircraft is threatened by grave and imminent danger and requests immediate assistance.	
By RTF	The Spoken Word **MAYDAY**
By Visual Signalling	The Signal **SOS** — Morse Code
	A Succession fo Pyrotechnic Lights Fired at Short Intervals each Showing a Single Red Light.
	A Parachute Flare Showing a Single Red Light.
By Sound Signalling (Other than RTF)	The Signal **SOS** — Morse Code
	A Continuous Sounding with any Sound Apparatus.

Urgency	
The following signals given together or separately, indicate that the commander of the aircraft has an urgent message to transmit concerning the safety of a ship, aircraft, vehicle or other property or of a person on board or within sight of the aircraft from which the signal is given.	
By RTF	The Spoken Word **PAN**
By Visual Signalling	The Signal **XXX** — Morse Code
By Sound Signalling (Other than RTF)	The Signal **XXX** — Morse Code

Safety	
The following signals, given either together or separately, before the sending of a message, signify that the commander of the aircraft wishes to give notice of difficulties which compel it to land but that he does not require immediate assistance.	
By RTF	No RTF Signal Designated
By Visual Signalling	A Succession of White Pyrotechnic Lights, *or*,
	The Repeated Switching On and Off of the Aircraft Landing Lights, *or*,
	The Repeated Switching On and Off of the Aircraft Navigation Lights (in an Irregular Manner).

Warning Signals to Aircraft in Flight

In the United Kingdom, the following signals shall respectively have the following meanings:

By Day	A series of projectiles discharged at intervals of ten seconds, each showing on bursting black or white smoke.
By Night	A series of projectiles discharged at intervals of ten seconds, each showing on bursting white lights or stars, or an intermittent white luminous beam directed at the aircraft.

These signals shall indicate that the aircraft to which the signal is directed is in the vicinity of an area which relates to national defence or one which otherwise concerns the public interest. A pilot must change course on receipt of the signal.

By Day or By Night	A series of projectiles discharged at intervals of ten seconds, each showing on bursting green lights or stars.

This signal shall indicate that the aircraft to which the signal is directed is in the vicinity of an area which relates to national defence or one which otherwise concerns the public interest. Upon receiving this signal, the commander of an aircraft should land at the nearest suitable aerodrome, and one which it can reach by flying to the least possible extent over the particular area.

Disasters in the UK FIRs — Restriction of Flying

In the event of a disaster occuring on land or at sea within the UK FIRs, the Emergency Controlling Authority (ECA), normally a represenative of one of the following agencies: Home Office; Department of Energy; HM Coastguard Headquarters; Edinburgh RCC; or Plymouth RCC, may find it necessary for the safety of life and property and particularly for the protection of those subsequently engaged in Search and Rescue action, to inhibit flight in the vicinity of the disaster by aircraft not directly engaged with emergency action.

On receipt of a request from the ECA, the initial action will normally be to establish by NOTAM Class I a temporary Danger Area around the scene of the incident. If the temporary Danger Area fails to achieve the objective, 'Restriction of Flying — Disaster — Regulations', which will make it an offence for an aircraft to be flown in the designated area without the permission of the ECA, will be brought into operation by NOTAM Class I.

Subject to any overriding considerations of safety, requests for overflight in the designated area from governmental and other official agencies, such as the Nature Conservancy Council, are to be given priority over requests from en-route traffic, company aircraft, the press and television.

 Extracts From the Rules of the Air and Air Traffic Control Regulations

Interpretation

The statutory document which covers these Rules and Regulations commences with an introductory paragraph defining some of the expressions used in the body of the document. This will permit the contents to be understood more clearly.

Many of these definitions have already been covered in the preceding paragraphs of this section but to avoid any misconceptions when reading the following pages, they are repeated below.

Air Traffic Control Clearance means authorisation by an Air Traffic Control Unit for an aircraft to proceed under conditions specified by that unit.

Anti-Collision Light means a flashing red light showing in all directions for the purpose of enabling the aircraft to be more readily detected by the pilots of distant aircraft.

Apron means the part of an aerodrome provided for the stationing of aircraft for the embarkation and disembarkation of passengers, the loading and unloading of cargo and for parking. This area is often called the *Parking Area*.

Ground Visibility means the horizontal visibility at ground level.

IFR Flight means a flight conducted in accordance with the Instrument Flight Rules.

Manoeuvring Area means the part of an aerodrome provided for the take-off and landing of aircraft and for the movement of aircraft on the surface, excluding the apron and any part of the aerodrome provided for the maintenance of aircraft.

The Order means the current Air Navigation Order (as amended).

Runway means an area, whether or not paved, which is provided for the take-off or landing run of aircraft.

VFR Flight means a flight conducted in accordance with the Visual Flight Rules.

Cloud Ceiling in relation to an aerodrome means the distance measured vertically from the notified elevation of that aerodrome (notified elevation will be found in the AGA section of the Air Pilot and on air navigation maps) to the lowest part of any cloud visible from the aerodrome which is sufficient to obscure more than one half of the sky so visible.

Night means the time between half an hour after sunset and half an hour before sunrise being determined at surface level.

Unless the context of the following Rules implies otherwise they shall have the same respective meanings as in the Air Navigation Order.

Application of Rules to Aircraft
These Rules, in so far as they are applicable in relation to aircraft, shall apply to:

1. *All aircraft within the United Kingdom.*

2. All aircraft registered in the United Kingdom, *wherever they may be.*

The application of this Rule has several purposes, two examples of which are:

To ensure as far as possible that foreign registered aircraft operating within the UK airspace system do so in a manner which conforms to the UK Air Traffic Regulations.

UK registered aircraft equipped to comply with these Rules and flying overseas may not always be equipped to meet certain requirements contained in foreign air legislation, therefore some basis must be laid down to permit the aircraft to continue its passage.

Reporting Hazardous Conditions
The commander of an aircraft shall, on meeting with hazardous conditions in the course of a flight, or as soon as possible thereafter, send to the appropriate air traffic control unit by the quickest means available information containing such particulars of the hazardous conditions as may be pertinent to the safety of other aircraft.

Hazardous situations are not common occurrences in an organised airspace system, but like certain illnesses can sometimes go unrecognised for a period of time or remain unrecognised completely until something happens.

Therefore although the principle behind this Rule is simple and self explanatory, it will sometimes require greater vigilance than is first appreciated in order to recognise the symptoms of a developing hazard to air safety, for example:

'Whereas the development of unreported thunderstorms is clearly a reportable hazard, the fact that a landing **T** is indicating a landing direction which is completely contrary to the wind direction may not be so easily recognised, but could nevertheless be as much a reportable hazard as a thunderstorm.'

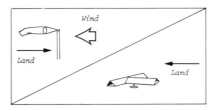

Low Flying
In as far as aeroplanes are concerned this Rule clearly states:

(a) An aeroplane shall not fly over any congested area of a city, town or settlement:

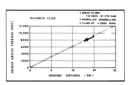

(i) Below such a height as would enable it to be flown clear of the area and land without incurring danger to persons or property in the event of engine failure;

or

(ii) Below a height of 1500' above the highest fixed object within 2000' of the aircraft,

whichever is the higher.

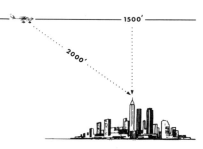

(b) An aircraft shall not fly:

(i) Over, or within 3000' of, any assembly in the open air of more than 1000 persons who are assembled for the purpose of witnessing or participating in any organised event, except with the permission in writing of the CAA and in accordance with any condition therein specified and with the consent in writing of the organisers of the event;

or

(ii) Below such a height as would enable it to alight clear of the assembly in the event of engine failure.

Clearly it would be difficult for a pilot to determine the number of persons forming such an assembly unless he has prior information, and because of this it is unlikely that a pilot would be prosecuted for breaking this Rule, providing he can prove that he was maintaining a reasonable height during the en-route phase of his flight, and that prior information regarding the existence of such an assembly was not promulgated.

500'

(c) An aircraft shall not fly closer than 500' to any person, vessel, vehicle or structure.

Due to the practical difficulties of definition, animals are not included in this Rule, but clearly cattle and horses etc., should be considered by a sensible pilot and he should keep well clear of them whenever possible.

Nothing in this Rule shall prohibit an aircraft from flying in such a manner as is necessary for the purpose of saving life. It should also be noted that (a) (ii) will not apply during that stage of any flight in which the pilot is acting according to a Special VFR Clearance, or along any route notified for the purposes of this Rule, e.g. Entry/Exit Lanes.

Further to this (c) will not be applicable if the aircraft is taking off or landing at an aerodrome in accordance with normal aviation practice. Nevertheless unless in emergency conditions, the approaches to land must be confined to the airspace customarily used for this purpose.

Simulated Instrument Flight

A pilot who wishes to qualify for the issue of a Night, IMC or Instrument Rating, or who wishes to obtain some practice in instrument flying, will have to undertake training for this purpose.

During this training, his vision will have to be suitably screened from external visual references, and such flying is known as simulated instrument flight. The following Rule has therefore been laid down to protect the safety of the aircraft and its occupants:

'An aircraft shall not be flown in simulated instrument flight conditions unless:

(a) The aircraft is fitted with dual controls which are functioning properly;

(b) An additional pilot (in this Rule called a safety pilot) is carried in a second control seat of the aircraft for the purpose of rendering such assistance as may be necessary to the pilot flying the aircraft;
and

(c) If the safety pilot's field of vision is not adequate both forward and to each side of the aircraft, a third person, being a competent observer, occupies a position in the aircraft which from his field of vision makes good the deficiencies in that of the safety pilot, and from which he can readily communicate with the safety pilot.

For the purposes of this Rule, the expression *'simulated instrument flight'* means a flight during which mechanical or optical devices are used in order to reduce the field of vision or the range of visibility from the cockpit of the aircraft.

Practice Instrument Approaches

Within the United Kingdom an aircraft shall not carry out instrument approach practice when flying in Visual Meteorological Conditions unless:

(a) The appropriate air traffic control unit has previously been informed that the flight is to be made for the purpose of instrument approach practice;
and

(b) If the flight is not being carried out in simulated instrument flight conditions, a competent observer is carried in such a position in the aircraft that he has an adequate field of vision and can readily communicate with the pilot flying the aircraft.

Light and Other Signals to be Shown or Made by Aircraft

All aircraft must display a minimum system of external lights when taxying or flying at night. These lights together with the appropriate colours are clearly laid down in Rule 9 of the Rules of the Air and Air Traffic Control Regulations.

In the interests of safety during night operations pilots must be able to distinguish between powered aircraft, gliders and balloons and for this reason, there are differences in the lighting systems of the varying classes of aircraft.

These differences are shown in Fig. 2-32 on page 2-61, and expanded in the following text.

Fig. 2-32

Display of Lights by Aircraft — By night, an aircraft shall display such of the lights specified in the Rules as may be appropriate to the circumstances and shall not display any other lights which might obscure or otherwise impair the visibility of, or be mistaken for, such lights. Provided that nothing in this paragraph shall prevent the display of an anti-collision light.

Flying Machines — A flying machine registered in the UK having a maximum total weight authorised of 5.700 kg or less, should when flying at night display the following system of lights:

    (a)   *(i)*   *A green light of at least 5 candela showing to the starboard side through an angle of 110° from dead ahead in the horizontal plane;*

          (ii)   *A red light of at least 5 candela showing to the port side through an angle of 110° from dead ahead in the horizontal plane,*
              and

(iii) *A white light of at least 3 candela showing through angles of 70° from dead astern to each side in the horizontal plane, all being steady lights;*

or

(b) *The lights specified in paragraph (a) and including an anti-collision light;*

or

(c) *The lights specified in paragraph (a) but all being flashing lights flashing together.*

Note:

Other lighting systems are mentioned in the Rules of the Air and Air Traffic Control Regulations, but these are not covered in this manual as they mainly concern large aircraft.

Flying Machines on the Ground — *A flying machine on a land aerodrome in the UK at which aircraft normally land or take-off at night shall, unless it is stationary on the apron or part of the aerodrome provided for the maintenance of aircraft, display by night either the lights which it would be required to display if it were flying, or such other lights as may be specified in the Rules of the Air and Air Traffic Control Regulations.*

Failure of Navigation Lights — *In the United Kingdom, in the event of the failure of any light which is required by the Rules to be displayed in flight, if the light cannot be immediately repaired or replaced the aircraft shall land as soon as in the opinion of the commander of the aircraft it can safely do so, unless authorised by the appropriate Air Traffic Control Unit to continue its flight.*

Although anti-collision lights or strobe lights are not a requirement for small aircraft, the use of such additional lighting systems will enhance safety. However, when using these lights and flying close to, or in cloud, it is advisable to switch them off to avoid possible distractions or even spatial disorientation to the pilot.

Gliders — *A glider while flying at night shall display either a steady red light of at least 5 candela, showing in all directions, or lights in accordance with paragraph (a) page 2-61.*

Free Balloons — *A free balloon while flying at night shall display a steady red light of at least 5 candela showing in all directions, suspended not less than 5 metres and not more than 10 metres below the basket, or if there is no basket, below the lowest part of the balloon.*

Captive Baloons and Kites —

(1) A captive baloon or kite while flying at night at a height exceeding 60 metres above the surface shall display lights as follows:

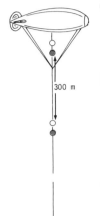

300 m

(a) A group of two steady lights consisting of a white light placed 4 metres above a red light, both being of at least 5 candela and showing in all directions. The white light being placed not less that 5 metres or more than 10 metres below the basket, or if there is no basket, below the lowest part of the balloon or kite.

(b) On the mooring cable, at intervals of not more than 300 metres measured from the group of lights referred to in sub-paragraph (a) of this paragraph, groups of two lights of the colour and power and in the relative positions specified in that sub-paragraph, and, if the lowest group of lights is obscured by cloud, an additional group below the cloud base;

and

(c) On the surface, a group of three flashing lights arranged in a horizontal plane at the apexes of a triangle, approximately equilateral, each side of which measures at least 25 metres; one side of the triangle shall be approximately at right angles to the horizontal projection of the cable and shall be delimited by two red lights; the third light shall be a green light so placed that the triangle encloses the object on the surface to which the balloon or kite is moored.

(2) A captive balloon while flying by day at a height exceeding 60 metres above the surface shall have attached to its mooring cable at intervals of not more than 200 metres measured from the basket, or, if there is no basket, from the lowest part of the balloon, tubular streamers marked with alternate bands of red and white.

(3) A kite flown in the circumstances referred to in paragraph (2) of this Rule shall have attached to its mooring cable either:

(a) Tubular streamers as specified in paragraph (2) of this Rule, or

(b) Streamers at not more than 100 metre intervals measured from the lowest part of the kite.

Airships —

(1) Except as provided in paragraph (2) of this Rule, an airship while flying at night shall display the following steady lights:

(a) A white light of at least 5 candela showing through angles of 110° from dead ahead to each side in the horizontal plane;

(b) A green light of at least 5 candela showing to the starboard side through an angle of 110° from dead ahead in the horizontal plane;

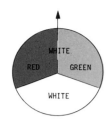

(c) A red light of at least 5 candela showing to the port side through an angle of 110° from dead ahead in the horizontal plane;

and

(d) A white light of at least 5 candela showing through angles of 70° from dead astern to each side in the horizontal plane.

(2) An airship while flying at night shall display, if it is not under command, or has voluntarily stopped its engines, or is being towed, the following steady lights:

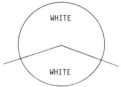

(a) The white lights referred to in paragraph (1) (a) and (d) of this Rule;

(b) Two red lights, each of at least 5 candela and showing in all directions suspended below the control car so that one is at least 4 metres above the other and at least 8 metres below the control car;

and

(c) If the airship is making way but not otherwise, the green and red lights referred to in paragraph (1) (b) and (c) of this Rule:

Provided that an airship while picking up its moorings, notwithstanding that it is not under command, shall display only the lights specified in paragraph (1) of this Rule.

(3) An airship, while moored within the UK by night, shall display the following lights:

(a) When moored to a mooring mast, at or near the rear a white light of at least 5 candela showing in all directions;

(b) When moored otherwise than to a mooring mast:

(i) A white light of at least 5 candela showing through angles of 110° from dead ahead to each side in the horizontal plane;

(ii) A white light of at least 5 candela showing through angles of 70° from dead astern to each side in the horizontal plane.

(4) An airship while flying by day, if it is not under command, or has voluntarily stopped its engines, or is being towed, shall display two black balls suspended below the control car so that one is at least 4 metres above the other and at least 8 metres below the control car.

(5) For the purposes of this Rule:

(a) An airship shall be deemed not to be under command when it is unable to execute a manoeuvre which it may be required to execute by or under these Rules;

(b) An airship shall be deemed to be making way when it is not moored and is in motion relative to the air.

General Flight Rules

Knowledge of the actual weather and forecast weather conditions en-route and at destination is of vital concern to the pilot and he is reponsible for obtaining such weather information whenever practical before setting off on a planned flight.

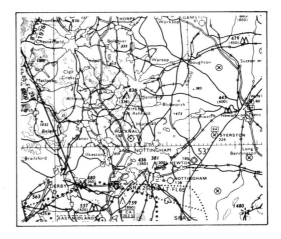

The General Flight Rules lay down the following:

Weather Reports and Forecasts

(1)   Immediately before an aircraft flies, the commander of the aircraft shall examine the current forecasts and reports of the weather conditions on the proposed flight path, being reports and forecasts which it is reasonably practicable for him to obtain, in order to determine whether Instrument Meteorological Conditions prevail or are likely to prevail during any part of the flight.

(2)   An aircraft which is unable to communicate by radio with an air traffic control unit at the aerodrome of destination shall not begin a flight to an aerodrome within a control zone if the information which is reasonably practicable for the commander of the aircraft to obtain indicates that it will arrive at that aerodrome when the ground visibility is less than 5 nautical miles or the cloud ceiling is less than 1500 feet, unless the commander of the aicrcraft has obtained from an Air Traffic Control Unit at that aerodrome permission to enter the aerodrome traffic zone.

  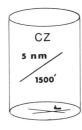

Rules for Avoiding Aerial Collisions

For the same reasons that road traffic have to obey certain rules, e.g. they must be driven on a particular side of the road, so aircraft must abide by the same principles and follow specific rules adapted to their environment.

(1)   General

(a)   Notwithstanding that the flight is being made with Air Traffic Control clearance it shall remain the duty of the commander of an aircraft to take all possible measures to ensure that his aircraft does not collide with any other aircraft.

(b)   An aircraft shall not be flown in such proximity to other aircraft as to create a danger of collision.

(c) Aircraft shall not fly in formation unless the commanders of the aircraft have agreed to do so.

(d) An aircraft which is obliged by these Rules to give way to another aircraft shall avoid passing over or under the other aircraft, or crossing ahead of it, unless passing well clear of it.

Note: The reason for Rule (d) is to avoid situations where pilots of opposing or converging aircraft simultaneously attempt to climb up or dive down in their attempts to remain clear of the other aircraft.

(e) An aircraft which has the right-of-way under this Rule shall maintain its course and speed.

(f) For the purpose of this Rule a glider and a flying machine which is towing it shall be considered to be a single aircraft under the command of the commander of the towing flying machine.

(2) *Aircraft which are Converging:*

(a) Subject to the provisions of paragraphs (3) and (4) of this Rule, an aircraft in the air shall give way to other converging aircraft as follows:

(i) Flying machines shall give way to airships, gliders and balloons;

(ii) Airships shall give way to gliders and balloons;

(iii) Gliders shall give way to balloons.

(b) Subject to the provisions of sub-paragraph (a) of this paragraph, when two aircraft are converging in the air at approximately the same altitude, the aircraft which has the other on its right shall give way:

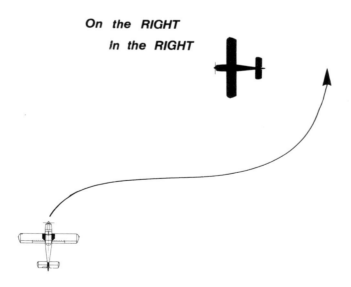

On the RIGHT

In the RIGHT

Provided that mechanically driven aircraft shall give way to aircraft which are towing other aircraft or objects.

(3)   Aircraft Approaching Head-On

When two aircraft are approaching head-on or approximately so in the air and there is a danger of collision, each shall alter course to the right.

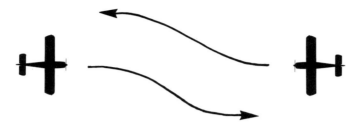

(4)   Aircraft Overtaking

An aircraft which is being overtaken in the air shall have the right-of-way and the overtaking aircraft, whether climbing, descending or in level flight, shall keep out of the way of the other aircraft by altering course to the right, and shall not cease to keep out of the way fo the other aircraft until the other aircraft has been passed and is clear, notwithstanding any change in the relative positions of the two aircraft.

Provided that a glider overtaking another glider in the United Kingdom may alter its course to the right or left.

(5)   Aircraft Landing

An aircraft while landing or on final approach to land shall have the right-of-way over other aircraft in flight or on the ground or water.

(6)   Two or more Aircraft Landing

In the case of two or more flying machines or gliders approaching any place for the purpose of landing, the aircraft at the lower altitude shall have the right-of-way, but it shall not cut in front of another aircraft which is on final approach to land or overtake that aircraft. Provided that:

(a)   When an Air Traffic Control Unit has communicated to any aircraft an order of priority of landing, the aircraft shall approach to land in that order,   and

(b)   When the commander of an aircraft is aware that another aircraft is making an emergency landing, he shall give way to that aircraft, and at night, notwithstanding that he may have received permission to land, shall not attempt to land until he has received further permission to do so.

Aerobatic Manoeuvres
An aircraft shall not carry out any aerobatic manoeuvre:

(a) *Over the congested area of any city, town or settlement; or*

(b) *Within controlled airspace except with the consent of the appropriate Air Traffic Control Unit.*

CLEAR OF TOWNS

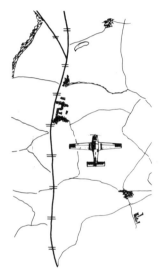

Right hand Traffic Rule
An aircraft which is flying within the United Kingdom in sight of the ground and following a road, railway, canal or coastline, or any other line of landmarks, shall keep such line of landmarks on its left.

Helicopters following certain landmarks may sometimes be exempt from this rule.

Notification of Arrival

(1) *The commander of an aircraft entering or leaving the United Kingdom on any flight for which a flight plan has been sumbitted shall take all reasonable steps to ensure upon landing that notice of the arrival of the aircraft is given to the aerodrome of departure.*

Provided that notice of arrival need not be given upon completion of flight between the United Kingdom and the Republic of Ireland or any other country in Europe or in or bordering on the Mediterranean Sea, unless an Air Traffic Control Unit at the aerodrome of departure has required it to be given, or unless the aircraft lands at an aerodrome other than its intended destination when it began the flight.

(2) *The commander of an aircraft who has caused notice of its intended arrival at any aerodrome shall ensure that the Air Traffic Control Unit or other authority at that aerodrome is informed as quickly as possible of any estimated delay in arrival of 45 minutes or more.*

Flight in Notified Airspace (Rule 21)
In relation to flights in Visual Meteorological Conditions in controlled airspace notified for the purposes of this Rule, the commander of an aircraft shall comply with Rules 27 and 28 of these Rules as if the flights were IFR flights.

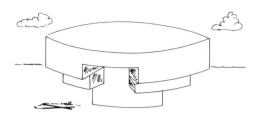

Provided that the commander of the aircraft shall not elect to continue the flight in compliance with the Visual Flight Rules for the purposes of Rule 27 (3).

Rules 27 and 28 relate to the filing of flight plans and obtaining Air Traffic Control clearance, and the making of position reports. Paragraph (3) of Rule 27 allows the pilot in certain circumstances to cancel his IFR flight plan and continue in accordance with the Visual Flight Rules.

Choice of VFR OR IFR
Subject to the provisions of Rule 21 of these Rules, an aircraft shall always be flown in accordance with the Visual Flight Rules or the Instrument Flight Rules:

Provided that in the United Kingdom, an aircraft flying at night:

(a) Outside a control zone shall be flown in accordance with the Instrument Flight Rules; or

(b) In a control zone shall be flown in accordance with the Instrument Flight Rules or the provisions of the proviso to Rule 23(b) of these Rules.

Rule 23(b) relates to the application of Visual Flight Rules in Controlled Airspace. This section of the the Rule states that an aircraft flying within controlled airspace in accordance with VFR must remain at least 1 nm horizontally and 1000' vertically away from cloud and in a flight visibility of at least 5 nm:

Provided that in a Control Zone, in the case of a Special VFR Flight, the aircraft shall be flown in accordance with any instructions given by the appropriate Air Traffic Control Unit.

For the purpose of this Rule **Special VFR Flight** means a flight made in Instrument Meteorological Conditions or at night in a Control Zone or at any time in a Control Zone notified for the purposes of Rule 21, or in any other airspace to which special rules apply, i.e. Special Rules Zones and Areas, in respect of which the appropriate Air Traffic Control Unit has given permission for the flight to be made in accordance with special instructions given by that unit instead of in accordance with the Instrument Flight Rules.

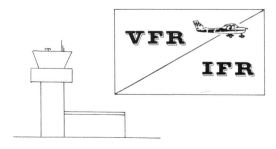

'This Page Intentionally Left Blank'

Aerodrome Traffic Rules

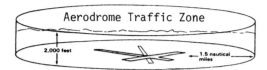

Application
In order to ensure the safe and expeditous movement of aircraft at aerodromes, certain Rules applicable to flying machines are established. These Rules must also be observed (whenever practical) by pilots of all other types of aircraft.

Visual Signals
The commander of a flying machine on, or in the traffic zone of, an aerodrome shall observe such visual signals as may be displayed at, or directed to him from the aerodrome by the authority of the person in charge of the aerodrome and shall obey any instructions which may be given to him by means of such signals.

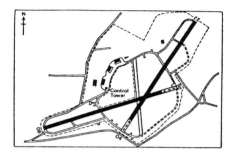

Provided that he shall not be required to obey Marshalling Signals if in his opinion it is inadvisable to do so in the interests of safety.

Access To and Movement On the Manoeuvring Area and Other Parts of the Aerodrome Used by Aircraft

(1)   A person or vehicle shall not go onto any part of an aerodrome provided for the use of aircraft and under the control of the person in charge of the aerodrome without the permission of the person in charge of the aerodrome, and except in accordance with any conditions subject to which that permission may have been granted.

(2)   A person or vehicle shall not go or move on the manoeuvring area of an aerodrome having an Air Traffic Control Unit without the permission of that unit, and except in accordance with any conditions subject to which that permission may have been granted.

(3)   Any permission granted for the purposes of this Rule may be granted either in respect of vehicles or persons generally, or in respect of any particular vehicle or person or any class of vehicle or person.

Right of Way on the Ground

(1)   This Rule shall apply to:
   (a)   Flying Machines.
   (b)   Vehicles.
   Such flying machines and vehicles being on any part of a land aerodrome provided for the use of aircraft and under the control of the person in charge of the aerodrome.

2-71

(2) Notwithstanding and Air Traffic Control clearance it shall remain the duty of the commander of an aircraft to take all possible measures to ensure that his aircraft does not collide with any other aircraft or with any vehicle.

(3) (a) Flying machines and vehicles shall give way to aircraft which are taking off or landing.

(b) Vehicles, and flying machines which are not taking off or landing, shall give way to vehicles towing aircraft.

(c) Vehicles which are not towing aircraft shall give way to aircraft.

(4) Subject to the provisions of paragraph (3) above, in case of danger of collision while taxying between two flying machines:

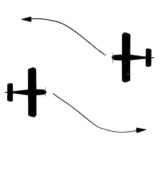

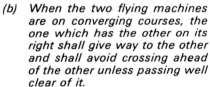

(a) When the two flying machines are approaching head-on or approximately so, each shall alter course to the right.

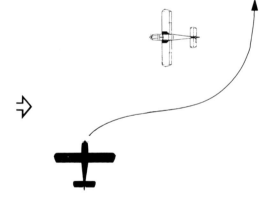

(b) When the two flying machines are on converging courses, the one which has the other on its right shall give way to the other and shall avoid crossing ahead of the other unless passing well clear of it.

(c) A flying machine which is being overtaken shall have the right-of-way, and the overtaking flying machine shall keep out of the way of the other flying machine by altering its course to the left until that other flying machine has been passed and is clear, notwithstanding any change in the relative positions of the two flying machines.

(5) Subject to the provisions of paragraph (3)(b) of the Rule a vehicle shall:

   (a) Overtake another vehicle so that the other vehicle is on the left of the overtaking vehicle.

   (b) Keep to the left when passing another vehicle which is approaching head-on or approximately so.

Dropping of Tow Ropes

Tow ropes, banners or similar articles towed by aircraft shall not be dropped from aircraft except at an aerodrome and:

   (a) *In accordance with arrangements made with an Air Traffic Control Unit at the aerodrome or, if there is no such unit, with the person in charge of the aerodrome or,*

   (b) *In the area designated by the marking shown here (a yellow cross), and the ropes, banners or similar articles shall be dropped when the aircraft is flying in the direction appropriate for landing.*

Aerodromes not having Air Traffic Control Units

(1) (a) *An aircraft shall not fly within a zone which the commander of the aircraft knows or ought reasonably to know to be the aerodrome traffic zone of an aerodrome where no Air Traffic Control Unit is for the time being notified as being on watch, except for the purpose of taking off or landing at that aerodrome or observing the signals in the signals area with a view to landing there, unless he has the permission of the person in charge of the aerodrome.*

   (b) *An aircraft flying within such a zone for the purpose of observing the signals shall remain clear of cloud and at least 500 feet above the level of the aerodrome.*

   Note: Good operating practice dictates that whenever an aircraft has to be flown overhead an aerodrome for the purpose of interpreting the signals area, it should be flown at or above 2000 feet above the aerodrome level. However the prevailing cloud base may make this impractical and the rules must therefore make provision for the aircraft to be flown at a lower height. Nevertheless this action should be considered the exception and not the rule.

(2) *The commander of an aircraft flying in such a zone or moving on such an aerodrome shall:*

   (a) *Conform to the pattern of traffic formed by other aircraft, or keep clear of the airspace in which the pattern is formed.*

   (b) *Make all turns to the left unless ground signals otherwise indicate; and*

   (c) *Take-off and land in the direction indicated by the ground signals or, if no such signals are displayed, into the wind, unless good aviation practice demands otherwise.*

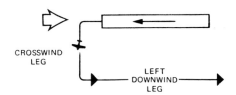

CROSSWIND LEG

LEFT DOWNWIND LEG

(3) (a) A flying machine or glider shall not land on a runway at such an aerodrome unless the runway is clear of other aircraft.

   (b) Where take-offs and landings are not confined to a runway —

   (i) A flying machine or glider when landing shall leave clear on its left any aircraft which has already landed or is already landing or is about to take-off; if such a flying machine or glider is obliged to turn, it shall turn to the left after the commander of the aircraft has satisfied himself that such action will not interfere with other traffic movements; and

Note: In the circumstances of (b)(i) above, a pilot of a high wing aircraft would be advised to stop and raise the aircraft flaps prior to turning left after landing. This will permit a greater field of vision behind him.

   (ii) A flying machine about to take-off shall take up position and manoeuvre in such a way as to leave clear on its left any aircraft which is already taking off or about to take-off.

(4) A flying machine after landing shall move clear of the landing area in use as soon as it is possible to do so.

Aerodromes Having Air Traffic Control Units

(1) An aircraft shall not fly within a zone which the commander of the aircraft knows or ought reasonably to know to be the aerodrome traffic zone of an aerodrome where an Air Traffic Control Unit is for the time being notified as being on watch, except for the purpose of observing any signals at that aerodrome with a view to landing there, unless he has the permission of the appropriate Air Traffic Control Unit.

(2) The commander of an aircraft flying in the aerodrome traffic zone of an aerodrome where an Air Traffic Control Unit is for the time being notified as being on watch or moving on such an aerodrome shall —

   (a) Cause a continuous watch to be maintained on the appropriate radio frequency notified for air traffic control communications at the aerodrome, or, if this is not possible, cause a watch to be kept for such instructions as may be issued by visual means;

   (b) Not taxi on the apron or manoeuvring area or take-off or land anywhere in the zone except with the permission of the Air Traffic Control Unit;

   (c) Comply with the provisions of the rule concerning **Aerodromes not having Air Traffic Control Units** paragraphs (1)(b), (2), (3) and (4), unless he has the permission of the Air Traffic Control Unit at the aerodrome, or has been instructed by that unit, to do otherwise.

(3) Without prejudice to the provisions of the rules relating to **Notification of Arrival** and **Flight Plans and Air Traffic Control Clearances**, the commander of an aircraft shall, immediately upon arrival at, or prior to departure from, an aerodrome within the United Kingdom having an Air Traffic Control Unit, ensure that such unit is informed of the flight which he has made or which he is about to undertake.

Special Rules for Certain Aerodromes
Certain aerodromes within the United Kingdom have air traffic movements of an intensity and type which in the interests of flight safety require protection greater than that afforded by the provision of an aerodrome traffic zone, yet which the requirement for a Control Zone or Terminal Area is not deemed to be necessary.

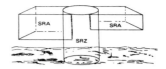

Such aerodromes are established with a Special Rules Zone usually accompanied with a Special Rules Area. Information on this type of airspace has already been covered on Pages 2-9 and 2-35.

The Rules of the Air and Air Traffic Control Regulations and the UK Air Pilot contain a list of aerodromes at which these Special Rules apply. The procedures to use in each case are also detailed in these two documents. It can however by noted here that the following procedures will apply in all cases.

(1) *For the purpose of these special rules for certain aerodromes,* **Special VFR Clearance** *means a clearance given by the appropriate Air Traffic Control Unit to an aircraft for flight within this special airspace. Such clearance will require that the aircraft remains clear of cloud, in sight of the surface and flown in accordance with any special instructions given by that unit.*

(2) *Unless otherwise authorised by the Air Traffic Control Unit at that aerodrome —*

   (a) *An aircraft shall not, during the notified hours of watch of the Air Traffic Control Unit at that aerodrome, fly within the notified airspace unless the commander of the aircraft, before so flying, obtains the permission of the Air Traffic Control Unit at the aerodrome and informs the Air Traffic Control Unit, on the notified radio frequency appropriate to the circumstances, of the aircraft's position, level and track; and*

   (b) *While an aircraft is within the notified airspace at any time during the notified hours of watch, the commander of the aircraft shall cause a continuous watch to be maintained on that frequency and comply with any instructions which the Air Traffic Control Unit at that aerodrome may give in the particular case.*

> The Rules of the Air and Air Traffic Control Regulations contain approximately 50 Rules of concern to pilots. This Manual does not define all these Rules in detail but the general contents of these Rules has been covered in this Section.

'This Page Intentionally Left Blank'

**Flight Safety
Extracts from:**

**Civil Aviation (Investigation of Accidents) Regulations 1969.
Air Navigation (Investigation of Combined Military and Civil Air Accidents) Regulations 1969.**

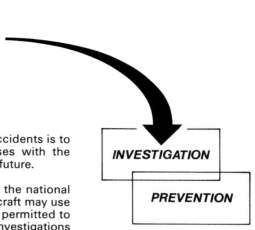

The main purpose of investigating aviation accidents is to determine the circumstances and the causes with the objective of avoiding such accidents in the future.

Because both military and civil air traffic use the national airspace system and the fact that military aircraft may use certain civil aerodromes and civil aircraft are permitted to use certain military aerodromes, a number of investigations may occur where it is necessary to obtain evidence from both civil and military personnel. For this reason a separate statutory document as referred to in the heading of this section has been enacted.

Both the Civil Aviation Investigation of Accidents and the Combined Military and Civil Air Accident Regulations have many common areas and the following regulations apply to both.

Notifiable Accidents
An accident shall be notified if, between the time when any person boards an aircraft with the intention of flight and such time as all persons have disembarked from the aircraft.:

(a) Any person suffers death or serious injury whilst in or upon the aicraft or by direct contact with the aircraft or anything attached thereto,   or

(b) The aircraft receives substantial damage.

Note: Substantial damage includes any damage or structural failure which adversely affects the structural strength, performance or flight characteristics of the aircraft and which would normally require the major repair or replacement of the affected component.

When a notifiabe accident occurs it is the duty of the aircraft commander to furnish a report but in the event of the commander being killed or incapacitated this report must be made by the operator of the aircraft.

The report must be communicated to the Accident Investigation Branch of The Board of Trade by the quickest means available and when the accident occurs within the UK the local police authorities must also be informed.

The report should commence with the identifying abbreviation ***ACCID*** and must contain (as far as possible) the following information:

Type, model, nationality and registration marks of the aircraft.

Name of the owner, operator and hirer, if any, of the aircraft.

Name of the commander of the aircraft.

Date and time (Greenwich Mean Time) of the accident.

Last point of departure and next point of intended landing.

Position of the aircraft with reference to some easily defined geographical point.

Number of persons on board the aircraft at the time of the accident.

Number of those persons killed as a result of the accident.

Number of those persons seriously injured as the result of the accident.

Number of persons killed or seriously injured elsewhere than on the aircraft.

Nature of the accident and brief particulars of the damage to the aircraft as far as is known.

Flight Safety Bulletin

This bulletin is issued quarterly by The General Aviation Safety Committee to all owners of UK registered aircraft and to Flying Training Organisations.

It contains useful information relating to the avoidance of accidents and should be read by all student and private pilots.

Accidents to Aircraft on the British Register (CAA Annual Publication)

The CAA publishes an annual survey, which includes statistical information together with short briefs on the aircraft accidents which occurred during the particular year.

The information published in this survey is divided into *classes of aircraft* operation and includes the accidents which occurred to aircraft being used in Club, Group and Training activities.

AIB Bulletins

The Accident Investigation Branch of the Board of Trade produce a monthly summary of aircraft accidents in the form of specific information concerning the type of aircraft, date and time of accident, type of flight, damage and/or injuries sustained by the occupants. Short summaries of individual accidents are also included.

Pink Aeronautical Information Circulars
The Aeronautical Information Service distributes aviation circulars covering many aspects of aircrew licensing and aircraft operations. The circulars which directly concern matters relating to aviation safety are coloured pink.

These circulars are available to all pilots and are obtainable from **AIS, Tolcarne Drive, Pinner, Middlesex, HA5 2DU.**

Summary
If pilots are to conduct safe and efficient flight operations, they must be made aware of all the factors which affect flight safety. Such factors range from those which concern the physical and psychological aspects of flying, the mechanical aspects of the aircraft and the environment in which both aircraft and pilots operate.

Only by keeping himself up to date in these three areas can a pilot expect to function safely and efficiently. It is therefore the responsibility of all aircrew to read and absorb the various facts concerning how accidents have occurred as well as following the advice given in the relevant publications.

The CAA has implemented a mandatory incident reporting system to ensure widespread dissemination of information which could be of value to pilots. The occasions when such reports should be made, together with the appropriate forms, can be obtained from most Flying Training Organisations.

In addition to the mandatory incident reporting system, each issue of the GASC Flight Safety Bulletin contains an Aircraft Occurrence Report Form and should a pilot experience an occurrence which in his opinion adversely affects flight safety he should complete and post this form to the General Aviation Safety Committee. This action will ensure that the information is received by those whose primary interest is to protect the safety of all aircraft and those who fly in them.

Pilots, Owners and Operators will find it useful to know where to report various events; if the appropriate form is not available, the following table shows the addresses (at the time this Manual was printed) against the Accident or type of Incident, details should be sent by letter.

Accidents	By the quickest means available to Accidents Investigation Branch, Kingsgate House, 66-74 Victoria Street, London SW1E 6SJ (Phone: 01 212 5852, Telex: 811074 AFTN EGGCYL) and forthwith in the UK to the local police authority.

(See Civil Aviation (Investigation of Accidents) Regulations 1969 also available as Section 8 of CAP 393 – Air Navigation Order and Regulations and AIC 24/1979 – Duty to Report Aircraft Accidents).

Airmisses	Immediate radio reports to ATS Unit with which the pilot is in communication, or if this is not possible by phone or other means to any UK ATS unit but preferably to an ATCC.

UK Airspace	Form CA1094 to Joint Airmiss Section, Hillington House, Uxbridge, Middlesex UB10 0RU
Foreign Airspace	Form CA1094 to relevant Foreign Authority with a copy to CAA Safety Data & Analysis Unit, Brabazon House, Redhill, Surrey RH1 1SQ

(See UK Air Pilot RAC 3-1-8 Section 7 and AIC 92/1978 – Airmiss Reporting).

Reportable Occurrences (including human factors, engineering, flight handling & ATC incidents in UK airspace)	Form CA1673 to CAA Safety Data & Analysis Unit, Brabazon House, Redhill, Surrey RH1 1SQ.

(See ANO Art 79, CAP 382 – Mandatory Occurrence Reporting Scheme and AIC 23/1979 – Reporting of Occurrences).

ATC Incidents (Foreign Airspace)	Form CA1673 to relevant Foreign Authority with a copy to CAA Safety Data & Analysis Unit, Brabazon House, Redhill, Surrey RH1 1SQ.

(See AIC 5/1979 – Reporting of Birdstrikes on Aircraft).

Wake Turbulence	Civil Aviation Authority, TRD3, CAA House, 43-59 Kingsway, London WC2B 6TE.

Student's Notes

Student's Notes

Student's Notes

Student's Notes

PROGRESS TESTS

This section contains a series of Progress Tests designed to enable you to test your level of knowledge in the subject material included in this Manual.

You should bear in mind the following points when completing the tests:

> They are designed to enable you to monitor your progress. Their objective is to provide a means whereby you can assess your knowledge and understanding at various stages in your learning task. If you can score good marks (75% or above) in these tests you will be able to sit the CAA written examination with a high degree of confidence.

> The test items are not trick questions, each statement means exactly what it says. Therefore read each question, response or statement carefully and do not look for hidden meanings.

> Be sure that you understand what the test item asks, and then review the alternate responses. Following this, decide which response is the correct one or work out the problem to obtain the correct answer.

> Always select the response which gives the most complete and correct answer, the others will be responses which are totally wrong, partially wrong or those which you might select if you lack sufficient knowledge of the subject.

> Upon completing each test, check your answers against those shown on page Q27. Questions which give you difficulty or which you fail to answer correctly will give you an indication of those areas in which you lack understanding, and you should therefore review the appropriate parts of the subject before proceeding with your next stage of study.

QUIZ No. 1

SUBJECT – Air Legislation

(1) The statutory documents which cover the privileges of private pilots and the general flight procedures to be used by all pilots, are:

(a) The Civil Air Publication 85.
The Rules of the Air and Air Traffic Control Regulations.
The (General) Air Navigation Regulations.

(b) The Air Navigation Order.
CAP 53.
CAP 413

(c) The Air Navigation Order.
The Air Navigation (General) Regulations.
The Rules of the Air and Air Traffic Control Regulations.

(d) All the above publications are statutory documents.

(2) The Civil Air Publications 413, 53 and 85:

(a) Only cover those ATC procedures which are applicable to pilots who hold Private Pilot Licences.

(b) All contain information of relevance to the private pilot.

(c) Contain those schedules which are outlined in the Air Navigation Order.

(d) Are documents which have been enacted by Parliament.

(3) In relation to the classification of aircraft:

(a) The term aircraft, only applies to *'heavier than air machines'*.

(b) An airship is defined as an aircraft which is *'heavier than air'*.

(c) Kites and balloons are described as *'non-mechanically driven aircraft which are heavier than air'*.

(d) The classes of aeroplanes are:
Motor glider.
Amphibian.
Seaplane.
Landplane.
Microlight.

Q1

(4) A Certificate of Airworthiness must be valid during the period:

(a) In which the particular aircraft is flown with passengers on board.

(b) At all times when the aircraft is flown, with the exception of those flights during which the aircraft is undergoing test or acceptance flights.

(c) Whenever the aircraft is being flown for Hire and Reward.

(d) All of the above responses contain correct information.

(5) A Certificate of Airworthiness:

(a) Will contain the name and address of the owner of the aircraft.

(b) Will contain the registration letters of the aircraft to which it relates.

(c) Will only be issued for an aircraft which is cleared to undertake Public Transport operations.

(d) If issued in the *Special Category* will be valid for a fixed period of 3 years.

(6) The Certificate of Airworthiness for an aircraft in the Public Transport Category will normally be issued for:

(a) A period of 1 year.

(b) A period of 6 months.

(c) A period of 3 years.

(d) An indefinite period.

(7) An aircraft issued with a *Special Category* Certificate of Airworthiness may be used for:

(a) Public Transport operations.

(b) Any purpose.

(c) Any purpose provided certain maintenance conditions are complied with.

(d) Any purpose (other than Public Transport or flying training for reward), specified in the C of A but not including the carriage of passengers unless expressly permitted.

(8) The CAA may issue a Certificate of Airworthiness subject to the aircraft being operated in accordance with certain conditions. These conditions will be:

(a) Found by reference to the Owner's Manual or equivalent Manual.

(b) Stated on the Certificate of Airworthiness.

(c) Shown on the Certificate of Registration.

Indicated in the appropriate Maintenance Schedule.

(9) In relation to the aircraft Owner's Manual, Flight Manual or Pilot's Operating Handbook:

(a) A code number will be marked on the appropriate Manaul or Handbook which is the same as the code number shown on the aircraft Certificate of Airworthiness.

(b) It will not be necessary to conform to the Emergency Procedures laid down in these documents.

(c) Information concerning the operation of the aircraft is not necessarily contained in these documents.

(d) All the above responses are incorrect.

(10) A Certificate of Maintenance will be issued:

(a) Annually for individual Aircraft.

(b) Upon the satisfactory completion of each required Servicing Inspection.

(c) At the time of issue of the aircraft's Certificate of Airworthiness and will remain effective for two years.

(d) Every 6 months regardless of the flying hours completed by the aircraft concerned.

'This page intentionally left blank'

ANSWER SHEET

QUIZ No. 1

Q	A
1	
2	
3	
4	
5	
6	
7	
8	
9	
10	

QUIZ No. 2

SUBJECT – Air Legislation

(1) If a pilot during flight, fails to observe or acts contrary to the conditions or requirements included in the relevant Certificate of Airworthiness:

(a) It will constitute a breach of the regulations.

(b) The pilot will be liable to a fine and/or imprisonment.

(c) The insurance policy of the aircraft will be invalidated during the continuance of the breach.

(d) All the above responses are correct.

(2) The validity periods for all Certificates of Airworthiness:

(a) Will last for two years.

(b) Are non-expiring.

(c) Will last for one year.

(d) Will be related to the Category in which the Certificate of Airworthiness is issued.

(3) The equipment which is required to be carried in relation to the circumstances of flight is:

(a) Laid down in the Owner's Manual or equivalent document.

(b) Itemised on the rear side of the Certificate of Airworthiness.

(c) Detailed in tabular form in the Air Navigation Order.

(d) Left to the discretion of the 'Pilot in Command'.

(4) The scale of radio equipment required according to the circumstances of flight can be found:

(a) On the rear page of the Certificate of Airworthiness.

(b) On the aircraft 'Radio Licence'.

(c) On the Certificate of Approval of Radio Installation.

(d) In a Schedule of the Air Navigation Order.

(5) In relation to the Flight Radiotelephony Operators Licence, which of the following is correct:

(a) This licence must be held by anyone operating an aircraft radio installation.

(b) The licence is a requirement to conduct cross country flights.

(c) This licence must be held by Student and Private Pilots.

(d) Dispensation is given to Student Pilots so that they can legally operate an aircraft radio without holding this licence.

(6) Aircraft and Engine Log Books are:

(a) Not required to be maintained by an aircraft owner or operator.

(b) Maintained for each aircraft in order to record flight times and any servicing, repair or modification carried out.

(c) Not required to show the flight times completed by the particular aircraft.

(d) Not required to show the servicing work done to an aircraft unless a 'Check Certificate' is to be issued.

(7) In relation to an aircraft Weight Schedule:

(a) The basic weight of an aircraft consists of, the weight of the empty aircraft together with the weight of the fuel and oil to be carried.

(b) All aeroplanes for which a Certificate of Airworthiness is issued must be weighed and have the centre of gravity position determined.

(c) The basic weight of an aircraft consists of, the empty weight of the aircraft, including the unusable fuel and oil, and any fixed items of equipment which are listed on the Weight Schedule plus the weight of the flight crew.

(d) A Weight Schedule must be preserved for a minimum period of two years following the next occasion on which the aircraft is weighed.

(8) A pilot who suffers an injury or illness:

(a) Must not fly as 'Pilot in Command' for at least 6 days.

(b) Must inform the CAA if the injury or illness prevents him from acting as a member of flight crew for a period of 7 days.

(c) Must not fly as 'Pilot in Command' for at least 10 days.

(d) Must inform the CAA if the injury or illness incapacitates him from acting as a member of flight crew for a period of at least 20 days.

(9) The privileges of a Student Pilot will permit:

(a) The holder of a current Student Medical Certificate to act as *'Pilot in Command'* during flights within the United Kingdom excluding the Channel Isles and the Isle of Man.

(b) Passengers to be carried but only when the flight is authorised by a flying instructor.

(c) The holder of a current Student Medical Certificate to act as *'Pilot in Command'* during flights within the United Kingdom, the Channel Isles and the Isle of Man.

(d) All the above responses are incorrect.

(10) In relation to the issue of a Private Pilot's Licence:

(a) The ground examinations and flight test must be completed within six months of commencing the course of training.

(b) The ground examinations and flight test must be completed within the six months immediately preceding the date of qualifying for the grant of the licence.

(c) THe ground examinations and flight test must be completed within the twelve months immediately preceding the date of qualifying for the grant of the licence.

(d) The licence will be issued without an *'Aircraft Rating'* unless the flight test has been satisfactorily completed.

(11) In order to renew the Certificate of Experience included in a Private Pilot's Licence the holder of the licence will have to carry out the following:

(a) 2 hours as *'Pilot in Command'* and 3 hours dual.

(b) Either 5 hours as *'Pilot in Command'* or 2 hours as *'Pilot in Command'* and 3 hours dual.

(c) A minimum of 5 hours *'Pilot in Command'*, or alternatively 3 hours as *'Pilot in Command'* plus sufficient dual flying with a qualified flying instructor to make the total up to 5 hours of flight time.

(d) Only the 5 hours as *'Pilot in Command'* can be accepted towards the flight time required for a renewal of the Certificate of Experience.

(12) Which of the following are authorised to renew Certificates of Experience:

(a) Any qualified flying instructor.

(b) A Chief Flying Instructor.

(c) A pilot who holds a Commercial Pilot's Licence.

(d) Only authorised Private Pilot Licence Examiners.

(13) The privileges accorded to the holder of a current Private Pilot's Licence include, flights with passengers outside controlled airspace and above 3000' amsl in weather conditions which are not less than:

(a) A flight visibility of 5 nm provided the aircraft remains clear of cloud and in sight of the surface.

(b) A flight visibility of 1 nm provided the aircraft is not flown closer to cloud than 1000' vertically and 1 nm horizontally.

(c) A flight visibility of 5 nm provided the aircraft is not flown closer to cloud than 1000' vertically and 1 nm horizontally.

(d) A flight visibility of 3 nm provided the aircraft is not flown closer to cloud than 1000' horizontally.

(14) For the purpose of private pilot licensing there are four Groups of aeroplanes. Which of the following responses correctly defines the Group indicated?

(a) **Group 'A'**   All single engined aeroplanes and some small multi engined aeroplanes of which the maximum total weight authorised does not exceed 5700 kg.

(b) **Group 'B'**   Certain types of aeroplanes having two engines (only) of which the maximum total weight authorised does not exceed 5700 kg.

(c) **Group 'A'**   Only types of single engined aeroplanes of which the maximum total weight authorised does not exceed 5700 kg.

(d) **Group 'C'**   All single engined aeroplanes of which the maximum total weight authorised exceeds 5700 kg.

(15) The privileges of a Private Pilot's Licence will last for:

(a) 13 months from the date of issue regardless of whether or not the medical certificate is renewed.

(b) A statutory period of 13 months from the date of the pilot's initial flight test.

(c) A period of 13 months including the remainder of the month in which the flight test was carried out.

(d) A period of 13 months, but only provided the pilot carries out 5 hours flying as 'Pilot in Command' during the period.

(16) If the holder of a Private Pilot's Licence has not flown as *'Pilot in Command'* for a period of 26 months after the expiry of his Certificate of Test or Experience and then wishes to renew his privileges, he will be required to:

(a) Obtain a further Certificate of Experience.

(b) Apply to the CAA for an extension to the normal period of his aircraft Rating.

(c) Undertake;
(i) Further training, including both dual and solo flying, and
(ii) A flight test, including a cross country flight of not less than 50 nm with a landing at destination and a return to the departure aerodrome.

(d) Merely apply for a further flight test.

(17) Details which must be entered in your personal flying log book are:

(a) Your name, address and particulars of your licence (if any).

(b) Your name and address, and flight information in the form of;
Date(s) of flight
Time of take-offs and landings
Flight duration and whether it was day flying, night flying or cross country flying.

(c) The type of aircraft flown together with its registration marks.
The capacity in which the licence holder acted during the flight.
The details of any flight test undertaken, if such test was required for the issue or renewal of the Rating.

(d) Although the items contained in responses (a) and (c) do not include all the information which must be logged, those items which are mentioned will be required for correct log book recording purposes.

(18) Flying Instruction is defined in the Air Navigation Order as:

(a) Any dual instruction given by a flying instructor as a part of a course of training to obtain a Pilot Licence or Rating.

(b) Any time an instructor is on board the aircraft, whether the person handling the controls has a licence or not.

(c) Including that time when an instructor is on board the aircraft and pilot is undergoing a *'Check Ride'* on an aircraft type which he has not flown before but is in the same *'Group'* as that currently contained in his licence.

(d) All the above responses are correct.

(19) The Air Navigation Order gives details of the Pre-flight Actions required of an aircraft commander prior to flight. Which of the following responses is *not* required by the Air Navigation Order:

(a) That sufficient fuel and oil are carried and that a safe margin has been allowed for such contingencies as getting lost, or having to divert.

(b) That a meteorological forecast has been obtained (whenever available) for the route to be flown.

(c) That the aircraft Log Books (engine and airframe) have been obtained so that they can be carried on the intended flight.

(d) That the load carried by the aircraft is so distributed and secured that it may safely be carried on the intended flight.

(20) A pilot should not fly as *'Pilot in Command'* unless a certain time has elapsed if he has consumed alcohol.
The minimum recommended time between consuming a small amount of alcohol and flying as *'Pilot in Command'* of an aircraft is:

(a) 24 hours.

(b) 8 hours.

(c) 4 hours.

(d) 12 hours.

IIIIIIIIIIIIIIIIIIIIIIIIIIIIIIIIIIIIIIIIIIIIIIIIIIIIIIIIIIIIIIIIIIIIIIIIII

ANSWER SHEET

QUIZ No. 2

Q	A
1	
2	
3	
4	
5	
6	
7	
8	
9	
10	

Q	A
11	
12	
13	
14	
15	
16	
17	
18	
19	
20	

QUIZ No. 3

SUBJECT – Air Traffic Rules and Services

(1) The names of the UK Flight Information Regions are:

(a) Scottish.
   English.

(b) Western.
   Eastern

(c) London.
   Scottish.

(d) Northern.
   London.

(2) Certain parts of the FIR's have been classified under some of the names given in the following responses.
   Which of the responses below is most correct:

(a) Controlled Airspace.
   Special Rules Airspace.
   Limited Airspace.

(b) Advisory Airspace.
   Aerodrome Traffic Zones.
   Special Control Zones.

(c) Controlled Airspace.
   Advisory Airspace.
   Special Rules Airspace.
   Military Aerodrome Traffic Zones.

(d) Military Aerodrome Traffic Zones.
   Uncontrolled Airspace.
   Special Terminal Areas.

(3) Control Zones are established around certain major aerodromes. The vertical dimensions of these zones extend from:

(a) The surface to a common fixed level of 10.000' amsl.

(b) A specified altitude to a specified altitude.

(c) A specified altitude to a common fixed level of 10.000' amsl.

(d) Ground level to a specified altitude.

(4) Control Areas known as Airways have been established across the U.K. The dimensions of these Airways in width and vertical extent are:

(a) 5 nm in width from a specified altitude to a specified upper limit.

(b) 10 nm in width from a specified altitude to a specified upper limit.

(c) 5 nm in width from the surface to 25.000' amsl.

(d) 10 nm in width from the surface to a specified upper limit.

(5) Terminal Control Areas normally extend from:

(a) Ground level to a specified upper limit.

(b) A specified altitude to a specified upper limit.

(c) A specified altitude to an upper limit which is coincident with the upper level of the attendant Control Zone.

(d) Ground level to various upper limits dependent upon the size of the TMA.

(6) A Special Rules Zone:

(a) Is always established in association with a Control Zone.

(b) Extends from the surface to a specified upper limit and has specific geographic dimensions.

(c) Extends from a specified height above the surface up to a specified altitude.

(d) Is normally established in association with a Terminal Control Area.

(7) A pilot operating in accordance with VFR and flying above 3000' amsl must have:

(a) A flight visibility of 5 nm and remain clear of cloud by 1000' vertically and 1 nm horizontally.

(b) A flight visibility of 3 nm and remain clear of cloud by 1000' vertically and 1 nm horizontally.

(c) A flight visibility of 3 nm and remain clear of cloud.

(d) A flight visibility of 1 nm and remain clear of cloud by 1000' vertically and 1 nm horizontally.

(8) In order for a private pilot to operate within the privileges of his licence whilst carrying passengers and flying in accordance with the Visual Flight Rules at or below 3000' amsl at an indicated airspeed of 140 knots or less, he must:

(a) Remain clear of cloud, in sight of the surface and in a flight visibility of 3 nm.

(b) Remain clear of cloud and in a flight visibility of 1 nm.

(c) Remain 1000' vertically and 1 nm horizontally clear of cloud and in a flight visibility of not less than 3 nm.

(d) Remain 1000' vertically and 1 nm horizontally clear of cloud and in a flight visibility of not less than 1.5 nautical miles.

(9) When operating under Instrument Flight Rules outside controlled airspace at between 3000' amsl and 24.000' amsl a pilot:

(a) Is recommended to fly in accordance with the Quadrantal Rule.

(b) Must fly in accordance with the Semi-Circular Rule.

(c) Must fly in accordance with the Quadrantal Rule.

(d) All the above responses are incorrect.

(10) Which ot the following responses is a correct cruising level for a pilot to operate at when flying in accordance with the Instrument Flight Rules above 3000' in uncontrolled airspace and on a magnetic track of 285 degrees.

(a) Flight Level 45.

(b) Flight Level 55.

(c) Flight Level 50.

(d) Flight Level 60.

|||||||||||||||||||||||||||||||||||||||||||||||||||||||||||||||||||||||||

'This page intentionally left blank'

ANSWER SHEET

QUIZ No. 3

Q	A
1	
2	
3	
4	
5	
6	
7	
8	
9	
10	

QUIZ No. 4

SUBJECT – Air Traffic Rules & Services

(1) *'Special VFR Flight'* is normally only applicable to flights made:

(a) Above 3000' amsl.

(b) In Terminal Areas.

(c) In Control Areas.

(d) In Airways.

(2) When operating on a Special VFR Clearance, the pilot:

(a) Will be expected to comply with the Quadrantal Rule.

(b) Will be responsible for complying with all ATC instructions and ensuring that his flight visibility permits him to determine his flight path and remain clear of all obstructions.

(c) Must remain in weather conditions which give him a flight visibility of at least 5 nm.

(d) Both responses (b) and (c) are correct.

(3) A Class II Notam contains information:

(a) Of a nature which requires it to be communicated quickly.

(b) Of a non-urgent nature.

(c) Which will only be sent by the AFTN.

(d) Which is normally transmitted to an aerodrome by telephone.

(4) The AGA Section of the UK Air Pilot contains information relating to:

(a) Rules of the Air and Air Traffic Services.

(b) Facilitation.

(c) Aerodromes.

(d) Aeronautical Charts.

(5) In relation to *'altimeter setting procedures'* which of the following responses is correct:

(a) Whenever the QNH is set on the altimeter datum the term *'height'* will be used.

(b) Whenever the QFE is set on the altimeter datum the term *'altitude'* will be used.

(c) Whenever the Standard Setting (1013 mb) is set on the altimeter datum the term *'cruising level'* will be used.

(d) Whenever the QNH is set on the altimeter datum the altimeter will indicate altitude above sea level.

(6) The UK FIR's contain a number of *'Altimeter Setting Regions'*. The pressure setting issued for each region is:

(a) The lowest forecast pressure which can be expected during each hourly period.

(b) The QNH of the highest aerodrome within each region.

(c) Calculated from the average QNH pressure setting of the aerodromes within each region.

(d) Issued every 3 hours.

(7) In relation to the use of *'altimeter settings'* which of the following responses is correct:

(a) The QFE is normally used for en-route flying to establish a common datum for the en-route separation of aircraft.

(b) The QNH is normally used for en-route flying to enable a pilot to maintain a safe clearance above the terrain.

(c) The QNH is normally used for operations within the circuit pattern of an aerodrome which is situated outside controlled airspace.

(d) The QFE is normally used to enable a pilot to maintain a safe clearance above the terrain during navigation flights.

(8) When the *'Standard Setting'* (1013 mb) is set on an altimeter and the aircraft is operated above 3000' amsl, the:

(a) Term *'altitude'* is used instead of *'height'*.

(b) Pilot will report his distance above the surface in terms of *'height'*.

(c) Term *'Standard Altitude'* is used to indicate the aircraft cruising level.

(d) Expression *'Flight Level'* is used to indicate the aircraft cruising level or the level through which it is passing.

9 In the following illustration, letters are used in place of the correct terms. From the responses shown below select the one which correctly interprets the letters.

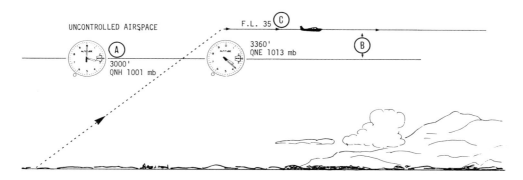

(a) A Transition Level
B Transition Height
C Transition Altitude.

(b) A Transition Altitude.
B Transition Level.
C The commencement of the Transition Layer.

(c) A Transition Level.
B Transition Layer.
C Transition Altitude.

(d) A Transition Altitude.
B Transition Layer.
C Transition Level.

10 When operating below Terminal Areas (excluding operations within an aerodrome circuit pattern) a pilot must use a particular altimeter setting to determine the base of the TMA. This setting is:

(a) The Area QNH of the associated ASR.

(b) The QFE of the major airport below the TMA.

(c) The QNH of any aerodrome situated below the particular TMA.

(d) The *'Standard Pressure Setting'*.

11 The horizontal and vertical dimensions of an Aerodrome Traffic Zone are:

(a) 3 nm horizontally from the aerodrome boundary and 2000' vertically from the aerodrome surface.

(b) 1.5 nm horizontally from the aerodrome boundary and 1500' vertically from the aerodrome surface.

(c) 3000 metres horizontally from the centre of the aerodrome and 2000' vertically from the aerodrome surface.

(d) 1.5 nm horizontally from the aerodrome boundary and 2000' vertically from the aerodrome surface.

(12) In relation to aerodromes:

(a) During the hours of operation of an aerodrome Air Traffic Unit a pilot must comply with the directions issued by Air Traffic Control unless he considers it unsafe to do so.

(b) A pilot must obtain prior permission to land at a military aerodrome.

(c) A pilot must obtain prior permission to use an aerodrome which is unlicensed.

(d) All of the above responses are correct.

At aerodromes, lamp signals may be used to direct aircraft within the Aerodrome Traffic Zone including the manoeuvring area.

(13) The lamp signal *'Steady Green'* directed at an aircraft in flight means:

(a) Return to the aerodrome and land.

(b) The aircraft is cleared to land.

(c) Land at this aerodrome and proceed to the parking area.

(d) The aircraft is cleared to return to the aerodrome but it should not land for the time being.

(14) The lamp signal used to indicate to an aircraft on the ground that is must move clear of the landing area is:

(a) A steady red.

(b) A series of green flashes.

(c) A series of white flashes.

(d) A series of red flashes.

At land aerodromes ground signals may be displayed for the guidance of air traffic.

(15) A white dumbell with black stripes superimposed on the circular portions indicates that aircraft:

(a) Must not land for the time being.

(b) Glider flying is in progress.

(c) Which are taking off or landing shall do so on a runway but that movement on the ground is not confined to paved, metalled or similar hard surfaces.

(d) Must only use paved, metalled or similar hard surfaces for take-off, landing or manoeuvring on the ground.

(16) The ground signal which indicates that aircraft may land on a special grass area delineated by white corner markings is:

(a) A white dumbell.

(b) A red **L**.

(c) A white cross.

(d) A white disc displayed alongside the cross arm of the Landing **T**.

(17) A red letter **L** displayed on a dumbell signifies that:

(a) Light aircraft are permitted to take-off and land either on a runway or on the area designated by a white letter **L**.

(b) The direction of take-off and landing do not necessarily coincide.

(c) Landing on this area is dangerous.

(d) Land in emergency only.

(18) Which of the following signals indicates that a *'Right Hand'* circuit is in force:

(a) A red and yellow striped arrow placed along two adjacent sides of the signals area.

(b) A red square panel with a diagonal strip.

(c) A yellow cross on a red square panel.

(d) A checkered flag or board.

At aerodromes, marshalling signals may be used to assist pilots manoeuvring their aircraft on the surface.

(19) The adjacent Marshalling Signal means:

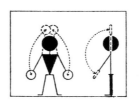

Arms repeatedly moved upward and backward, beckoning onward.

(a) Slow down.

(b) Start engine.

(c) All clear, marshalling finished.

(d) Move ahead.

The adjacent Marshalling
Signal means:

*Arms placed down, with
the palms towards the
ground then moved up
and down several times.*

(a)   All clear, marshalling finished.

(b)   Slow down.

(c)   This bay or parking area.

(d)   Release brakes.

ANSWER SHEET

QUIZ No. 4

Q	A
1	
2	
3	
4	
5	
6	
7	
8	
9	
10	

Q	A
11	
12	
13	
14	
15	
16	
17	
18	
19	
20	

QUIZ No. 5

SUBJECT – Air Traffic Rules & Services

(1) With reference to the filing of *'flight plans'* which of the following responses is correct:

(a) Flight plans must be filed at least 60 minutes prior to departure.

(b) Flight plans may only be filed for IFR flights.

(c) A private pilot may file a flight plan for any flight he undertakes.

(d) If for any reason a pilot who has filed a flight plan diverts or lands at an aerodrome not specified in his flight plan, it is his responsibility to ensure that the planned destination aerodrome is informed within 90 minutes of landing.

(2) In relation to Special VFR Clearances:

(a) These can only be obtained when Flight Plans are filed prior to the intended flight.

(b) A Special VFR Clearance can only be given to a pilot who holds an Instrument Rating.

(c) When using a radio equipped aircraft, a Special VFR Clearance may be requested during flight.

(d) A Special VFR Clearance can only be obtained by pilots who are operating radio equipped aircraft.

(3) In relation to *'Danger Areas'* the term *'day'* means:

(a) That time between 30 minutes after sunrise to 30 minutes after sunset, sunrise and sunset being determined at the surface.

(b) That period between 0800 and 1800 (GMT).

(c) That period between 0800 and 1800 (LMT).

(d) The time between sunrise and sunset (LMT).

(4) Information relating to *'Danger Areas'* is promulgated by various methods — which of the following responses gives the most correct list of information sources available to the pilot:

(a) The AGA Section of the UK Air Pilot.
Notams.
Aeronautical Information Circulars.

(b) The Chart of UK Airspace Restrictions.
Notams.
The RAC Section of the UK Air Pilot.

(c) The Air Navigation Order.
Notams.
Maps and Charts used in pilot navigation.

(d) The RAC Section of the UK Air Pilot.
The Chart of UK Airspace Restrictions.
Aeronautical Information Circulars.
Maps and Charts used for pilot navigation.

(5) The Code D406/15 in relation to a UK Danger Area means the Area when active extends from:

(a) The surface up to 1500' amsl.

(b) 1000' above the surface up to 5000' amsl.

(c) The surface up to 15.000' amsl.

(d) The lower limit is 1500' amsl and the upper limit wil be notified by Notam.

(6) Scheduled Danger Areas:

(a) Have their active periods notified by Notam.

(b) Have active periods which are permanently fixed.

(c) Are operational throughout any 24 hour period.

(d) Have their geographic dimensions shown on the Chart of UK Airspace Restrictions by a red pecked outline.

(7) Which of the following responses is correct:

(a) Prohibited Areas need only be avoided during the hours of daylight.

(b) Restricted Areas can only be entered with the permission of the controlling ATC unit.

(c) Only those obstructions which are considered hazards to air navigation are lighted.

(d) Gliding Sites are not normally shown on maps and charts used for pilot navigation.

(8) Details of Royal Flights are:

    (a) Notified to pilots through Aeronautical Information Circulars.

    (b) Only promulgated if the particular Royal Flight takes place outside Controlled Airspace.

    (c) Notified to pilots by issuing a Special RF Notam.

    (d) Both responses (b) and (c) are correct.

(9) Information relating to runway dimensions and lighting facilities at aerodromes, including Special Instructions, Restrictions and Warnings can be found in:

    (a) The COM Section of the UK Air Pilot and Notams.

    (b) The AGA Section of the UK Air Pilot and Notams.

    (c) The FAL Section of the UK Air Pilot.

    (d) The FAL Section of the UK Air Pilot and Notams.

(10) Which of the following is correct:

    (a) Aerodrome Beacons normally flash a Green light.

    (b) At civil aerodromes, Identification Beacons emit a Green light.

    (c) At military aerodromes an Identification Beacon normally emits a Green light.

    (d) At civil aerodromes, Identification Beacons sometimes emit a White light.

(11) The hours of availability of Customs facilities at Customs and Excise aerodromes:

    (a) Are given in the document "Air Traffic Control and Rules of the Air".

    (b) Will be found in the (RAC) Section of the UK Air Pilot.

    (c) Will be found in the (FAL) Section of the UK Air Pilot.

    (d) All the above responses are incorrect.

(12) The adjacent signal is one of the International Ground/Air Visual Signals. It means:

(a) Medical supplies are required.

(b) Aircraft seriously damaged.

(c) Unable to proceed.

(d) Probably safe to land here.

(13) In relation to the Distress, Urgency or Safety Signals established for the use of aircraft, which of the following responses is correct:

(a) A succession of pyrotechnic lights fired at short intervals each showing a Red light means that the commander of the aircraft wishes to give notice of difficulties which compel the aircraft to land but that immediate assistance is not required.

(b) A succession of White pyrotechnic lights means that an aircraft is threatened by grave and imminent danger but does not require immediate assistance.

(c) The repeated switching 'On' and 'Off' of the aircraft landing lights means that the aircraft is threatened by grave and imminent danger and requests immediate assistance.

(d) A succession of Red pyrotechnic lights fired from an aircraft signify that the aircraft is threatened by grave and imminent danger and requests immediate assistance.

(14) In relation to the Visual Flight Rules and the Instrument Flight Rules and their application to aircraft operations outside Controlled Airspace in the UK an aircraft:

(a) Must be flown either in accordance with the Visual Flight Rules or the Instrument Flight Rules.

(b) Can only be operated as directed by an Air Traffic Control Unit.

(c) Cannot be operated in accordance with Instrument Flight Rules when flying within an Aerodrome Traffic Zone.

(d) Must always remain clear of cloud by 1 nm horizontally and 1000' vertically and in a flight visibility of at least 5 nm in order to operate in accordance with the Visual Flight Rules.

(15) A flying machine registered in the UK having a maximum total weight authorised of 5.700 kg or less, should when flying at night display a system of lights as specified in the Rules of the Air and Air Traffic Control Regulations.

In relation to aeroplanes which of the following responses outlines an acceptable lighting system:

(a) A Green light showing to the port side through an angle of 110° from dead ahead in the horizontal plane.
A Red light showing to the starboard side through an angle of 110° from dead ahead in the horizontal plane.
A White light showing through angles of 70° from dead astern to each side in the horizontal plane.

(b) A Red light showing to the port side through an angle of 110° from dead ahead in the horizontal plane.
A Green light showing to the starboard side through an angle of 110° from dead ahead in the horizontal plane.
A White light showing through angles of 110° from dead astern to each side in the horizontal plane.

(c) A Green light showing to the starboard side through an angle of 110° from dead ahead in the horizontal plane.
A Red light showing to the port side through an angle of 110° from dead ahead in the horizontal plane.
A White light showing through angles of 70° from dead astern to each side in the horizontal plane.

(d) All the above responses are incorrect.

(16) Which of the following responses is correct:

(a) An aeroplane shall not fly over any congested area of a city, town or settlement, below a height of 1500' above the higest fixed object within 2000 metres of the aircraft.

(b) An aircraft shall not fly closer than 500' to any person, vessel, vehicle or structure.

(c) An aircraft shall not fly without written consent, over or within 2000' of any assembly in the open air of more than 1000 persons who are assembled for the purpose of witnessing or participating in an organised event.

(d) All the above responses are correct.

(17) An aircraft which is flying in sight of the ground and following a road, railway, canal or coastline, or any other line of landmarks:

(a) Shall keep such line of landmarks on its right.

(b) May keep such line of landmarks on either the left or the right of the aircraft.

(c) Shall keep such line of landmarks on its left.

(d) Shall keep such line of landmarks on its left only if the visibility is less than 2 nm.

(18) In relation to overtaking another flying machine during taxying:

(a) The overtaking aircraft shall keep out of the way of the other flying machine by altering its course to the right.

(b) Both flying machines shall alter course to give way to each other.

(c) The overtaking aircraft must keep out of the way of the other flying machine by altering its course to the left.

(d) The overtaking aircraft must slow down and remain behind any aircraft which is being towed.

(19) Whilst flying over an aerodrome for the purpose of observing the Signals Area with a view to landing at the aerodrome, a pilot should whenever possible:

(a) Remain below 500' above ground level.

(b) Fly at least 2000' or more above aerodrome level.

(c) Remain at 1000' above aerodrome level.

(d) Fly below 1000' above aerodrome level.

(20) A pilot who wishes to operate in a Special Rules Zone or Special Rules Area:

(a) Must obtain prior ATC clearance to enter either of these types of airspace.

(b) Need only obtain an ATC clearance to enter a Special Rules Area if Instrument Meteorological Conditions prevail.

(c) Is exempt from complying with ATC instructions within a Special Rules Zone if Visual Meteorological Conditions prevail.

(d) Will not require an ATC clearance to enter either type of airspace provided he can operate clear of cloud by 1000' vertically and 1 nm horizontally and remain in a flight visibility of at least 5 nm.

IIIIIIIIIIIIIIIIIIIIIIIIIIIIIIIIIIIIIIIIIIIIIIIIIIIIIIIIIII

ANSWER SHEET

QUIZ No. 5

Q	A
1	
2	
3	
4	
5	
6	
7	
8	
9	
10	

Q	A
11	
12	
13	
14	
15	
16	
17	
18	
19	
20	

ANSWERS TO PROGRESS TESTS

QUIZ No. 1	
1	c
2	b
3	d
4	b
5	b
6	c
7	d
8	b
9	a
10	b

QUIZ No. 3	
1	c
2	c
3	d
4	b
5	b
6	b
7	a
8	a
9	c
10	a

QUIZ No. 2	
1	d
2	d
3	c
4	d
5	d
6	b
7	b
8	d
9	c
10	b
11	c
12	d
13	c
14	c
15	b
16	c
17	d
18	a
19	c
20	b

QUIZ No. 4	
1	c
2	d
3	b
4	c
5	d
6	a
7	b
8	d
9	d
10	c
11	d
12	d
13	b
14	d
15	c
16	b
17	a
18	a
19	d
20	b

QUIZ No. 5	
1	c
2	c
3	c
4	d
5	c
6	b
7	b
8	c
9	b
10	b
11	c
12	c
13	d
14	a
15	c
16	b
17	c
18	c
19	b
20	a

'This page intentionally left blank'

INDEX

V

W

Z